M M Bremner. 2/3.

To be returned to –

Miss B McCarthy,
Church St. Sec. Glo'
Schl.,
Stapleford

Class 113 Rifas

The Teaching of English Series

EIGHT MODERN PLAYS

No. 102

A. A. MILNE

From a pen-drawing by E. Heber Thompson, after a photograph by "Coster—Photographer of Men." (*Copyright*)

EIGHT MODERN PLAYS

Selected and Edited by
JOHN HAMPDEN

THOMAS NELSON & SONS LTD
LONDON AND EDINBURGH

First published September 1927
Reprinted 1927, 1928 (*twice*), 1929, 1930, 1931, 1933, 1934 (*twice*), 1935, 1937 (*twice*), 1938, 1939, 1940, 1941, 1942, 1943, 1944, 1945 (*twice*), 1946, 1947

CONTENTS

By the same Editor

BALLADS AND BALLAD-PLAYS
SIX MODERN PLAYS
SEVEN MODERN PLAYS
EIGHT MODERN PLAYS
NINE MODERN PLAYS
TEN MODERN PLAYS
THREE MODERN PLAYS AND A MIME
FOUR MODERN PLAYS
TWELVE MODERN PLAYS (Duckworth and Co.)

EIGHT MODERN PLAYS

PREFACE

If this little volume of one-act plays may claim any originality of plan, it is that though primarily intended for junior readers and actors, it does not consist of "plays for children" or of adaptations from novels. With one excellent exception, all the plays in the book were written for performance by adult actors in the professional theatre, but as they have been chosen for their appeal to junior forms as well as their quality, it is hoped that they will be found worth reading, studying, and acting for their own sake—and as an introduction to Shakespeare.

For all their instinctive appreciation of the dramatic form, the small boy and girl are too often baffled and bewildered by being plunged straight into *The Merchant of Venice* or *A Midsummer Night's Dream*. A Fourth Form boy, who had just been introduced to Shakespeare, spoke for many of his peers when he approached the master's desk with the dismayed question: "Please, sir, is ALL this book *Julius Cæsar*?" To meet this difficulty, to provide an introduction to the treasures of our dramatic literature, the modern one-act play may be used to very good effect, for it is free from archaism in thought and speech, arresting, quickly understood, and short enough to be acted or read in one lesson.

This book can be used simply as a reader; but if any suggestion as to method may be ventured, it is that the plays should be treated as plays—to be acted rather than to be read. Parts should be carefully assigned in advance, and the players encouraged to study them, and sometimes to learn them by heart, as they will frequently offer to do. It is of great help if the most important entrances, exits, and stage-movements are settled by the teacher or by a " producer " chosen from the form, and a " stage-manager " may be appointed to look after any simple furniture and properties which are used. The important point is that each " performance " should be an attempt at interpretation. However crude form-room conditions may be, the youthful imagination transforms them, rejoicing in the simplest equipment ; and acting so quickens interest and appreciation that immediately there are opportunities to give training in speech and movement and " team-work," and to develop a rudimentary understanding of dramatic structure and characterization.

J. H.

ACKNOWLEDGMENTS

The editor wishes to express his thanks to the following authors and publishers for permission to include their plays in this book :

Mr. Alfred Noyes and Messrs. Blackwood for *Robin Hood ;* Mr. W. Graham Robertson and Messrs. Heinemann for *The Slippers of Cinderella ;* Mr. Hermon Ould and Messrs. Samuel French for *The Discovery ;* Mr. Bernard Gilbert and Messrs. Samuel French for *Eldorado ;* The Honourable Maurice Baring and Messrs. Heinemann for *Catherine Parr ;* Mr. A. A. Milne and Messrs. Samuel French for *The Princess and the Woodcutter ;* Mr. Miles Malleson and Messrs. Allen and Unwin for *Michael ;* and especially Mr. J. A. Ferguson, for revising *Campbell of Kilmohr* (published by Messrs. Gowans and Gray) for this edition, and adding his Acting Notes.

The editor also desires to acknowledge once again his great indebtedness to Dr. Richard Wilson ; to the lending libraries of the British Drama League and the Village Drama Society ; to the British Drama League's Librarian, Miss Violet Clayton ; and to his wife.

THE PRINCESS AND THE WOODCUTTER

By A. A. Milne

CHARACTERS

The Woodcutter.
The Princess.
The King.
The Queen.
The Red Prince.
The Blue Prince.
The Yellow Prince.
Attendants.

The music for the play is published by Messrs. Samuel French, Ltd.

THE PRINCESS AND THE WOODCUTTER

THE WOODCUTTER'S SONG

Woodcutter—

A humble woodman I,
A plain hard-working peasant,
A simple soul, who on the whole
Finds life extremely pleasant.
I envy none to-day
His lofty rank or station,
Enough for me to have a free
And healthy occupation.

Refrain : Singing and swinging my axe
On the monarch uprearing,
Stroke upon stroke, till the oak
Crashes down in the clearing.
So shall I vanquish, perchance,
Both the haughty and splendid,
Love shall have brought them to naught
When the tale shall be ended.

In realms of faery lore
I need no guide or tutor,
And there, I learn, princesses yearn
To wed the humble suitor.

The truly noble mind
All outward show despises;
It is not rank, or wealth, or swank
That takes the highest prizes!

Refrain (As before).

The Woodcutter is discovered singing at his work, in a glade of the forest outside his hut. He is tall and strong, and brave and handsome; all that a woodcutter ought to be. Now it happened that the Princess was passing, and as soon as his song is finished, sure enough, on she comes.

Princess. Good-morning, Woodcutter.

Woodcutter. Good-morning.

[*But he goes on with his work.*]

Princess [*after a pause*]. Good-morning, Woodcutter.

Woodcutter. Good-morning.

Princess. Don't you ever say anything except good-morning?

Woodcutter. Sometimes I say good-bye.

Princess. You *are* a cross woodcutter to-day.

Woodcutter. I have work to do.

Princess. You are still cutting wood? Don't you ever do anything else?

Woodcutter. Well, you are still a Princess; don't *you* ever do anything else?

Princess [*reproachfully*]. Now, that's not fair, Woodcutter. You can't say I was a Princess yesterday, when I came and helped you stack your wood. Or the day before, when I tied up your hand where you had cut it. Or the day before that, when we had our meal together on the grass. Was I a Princess then?

Woodcutter. Somehow I think you were. Somehow I think you were saying to yourself, "Isn't it sweet of a Princess to treat a mere woodcutter like this?"

Princess. I think you are perfectly horrid. I've a good mind never to speak to you again. [*Turns* R.] And—and I would, if only I could be sure that you would notice I wasn't speaking to you.

Woodcutter. After all, I'm just as bad as you. Only yesterday I was thinking to myself how unselfish I was to interrupt my work in order to talk to a mere Princess.

Princess. Yes, but the trouble is that you *don't* interrupt your work.

Woodcutter [*interrupting it and going up to her with a smile*]. Madam, I am at your service.

Princess. I wish I thought you were.

Woodcutter. Surely you have enough people at your service already. Princes and chancellors and chamberlains and waiting-maids.

Princess. Yes, that's just it. That's why I want your help. Particularly in the matter of Princes.

Woodcutter. Why, has a suitor come for the hand of Her Royal Highness ?

Princess. Three suitors. And I hate them all.

Woodcutter. And which are you going to marry ?

Princess. I don't know. Father hasn't made up his mind yet.

Woodcutter. And this is a matter which father—which His Majesty decides for himself ?

Princess. Why, of course ! You should read the history books, Woodcutter. The suitors to the hand of a Princess are always set some trial of strength or test of quality by the King, and the winner marries his daughter.

Woodcutter. Well, I don't live in a palace, and I think my own thoughts about these things. I'd better get back to my work.

[*He goes on with his chopping.*]

Princess [*gently, after a pause*]. Woodcutter !

Woodcutter [*looking up*]. Oh, are you there ? I thought you were married by this time.

Princess [*meekly*]. I don't want to be married. [*Hastily*] I mean, not to any of those three.

Woodcutter. You can't help yourself.

Princess. I know. That's why I wanted *you* to help me.

Woodcutter [*going up to her*]. Can a simple woodcutter help a Princess?

Princess. Well, perhaps a simple one couldn't, but a clever one might.

Woodcutter. What would his reward be?

Princess. His reward would be that the Princess, not being married to any of her three suitors, would still be able to help him chop his wood in the mornings. . . . I *am* helping you, aren't I?

Woodcutter [*smiling*]. Oh, decidedly.

Princess [*nodding*]. I thought I was.

Woodcutter. It is kind of a great lady like yourself to help so humble a fellow as I.

Princess [*meekly*]. I'm not *very* great.

[*And she isn't. She is the smallest, daintiest little Princess that ever you saw.*]

Woodcutter. There's enough of you to make a hundred men unhappy.

Princess. And one man happy?

Woodcutter. And one man very, very happy.

Princess [*innocently*]. I wonder who he'll be. . . . Woodcutter, if *you* were a Prince, would you be my suitor?

Woodcutter [*scornfully*]. One of three?

Princess [*excitedly*]. Oh, would you kill the others? With that axe?

Woodcutter. I would not kill them in order to help His Majesty make up his mind about his son-in-law. But if the Princess had made up her mind—and wanted me——

Princess. Yes?

Woodcutter. Then I would marry her, however many suitors she had.

Princess. Well, she's only got three at present.

Woodcutter. What is that to me?

Princess. Oh, I just thought you might want to be doing something to your axe.

Woodcutter. My axe?

Princess. Yes. You see, she *has* made up her mind.

Woodcutter [*amazed*]. You mean—— But—but I'm only a woodcutter.

Princess. That's where you'll have the advantage of them when it comes to axes.

Woodcutter. Princess! [*He takes her in his arms.*] My Princess!

Princess. Woodcutter! My Woodcutter! My, oh so very slow and uncomprehending, but entirely adorable Woodcutter!

[*They sing together. They just happen to feel like that.*]

OUR FAIRY STORY

Duet: Woodcutter and Princess

Princess. My dear, brown man,
With your strength and grace,
And your most attractive face,
Do you wonder how my love for you began?
Well, I don't quite know,
But with those dear arms around me
I know my fate has found me.

Woodcutter. My own, fair maid,
With all heaven in your eyes,
Are we mad or truly wise
When the laws of courts and kings are disobeyed?
Let the world go by,
With its pride and pomp and glory,
We have made our fairy story.

Both. This is just our fairy story,
Every word of which is true,
Older than the hills around us,
Yet so wonderfully new.
All the stories worth the telling
Surely must be told by two,
Each must have the self-same ending,
" You love me and I love you."

Princess. My dear, brown man!
Just because I love you blindly
You must rule me very kindly,
For I mean to be obedient—if I can!
I'm a poor spoiled child,
And my future education
Will afford you occupation,
But I recognize my master underneath the toiler's tan.

Woodcutter. My own, fair maid,
I declare your very meekness
Is the measure of my weakness,
And my mastery will seldom be displayed.
For at one shy glance
From beneath those drooping lashes
All my airy kingship crashes.

Both. (As before).

Woodcutter [*the song finished*]. But what will His Majesty say?

Princess. All sorts of things. . . . Do you really love me, Woodcutter, or have I proposed to you under a misapprehension?

Woodcutter. I adore you!

Princess [*nodding*]. I thought you did. But I wanted to hear you say it. If I had been a simple peasant, I suppose you would have said it a long time ago?

Woodcutter. I expect so.

Princess [*nodding*]. Yes. . . . Well, now we must think of a plan for making mother like you.

Woodcutter. Might I just kiss you again before we begin ?

Princess. Well, I don't quite see how I am to stop you.

[*The Woodcutter picks her up in his arms and kisses her.*]

Woodcutter. There !

Princess [*in his arms*]. Oh, Woodcutter, Woodcutter, why didn't you do that the first day I saw you ? Then I needn't have had the bother of proposing to you. [*He puts her down suddenly.*] What is it ?

Woodcutter [*listening*]. Somebody coming. [*He peers through the trees and then says in surprise,*] The King !

Princess. Oh ! I must fly !

Woodcutter. But you'll come back ?

Princess. Perhaps.

[*She disappears quickly through the trees.*]

[*The Woodcutter goes on with his work, and is discovered at it a minute later by the King and Queen. The music of " Tête à Tête " is played for the entrance. There enter first one red and one black attendant, walking backwards and bowing to the King and Queen. They are followed by two other attendants.*]

King [*puffing*]. Ah ! and a seat all ready for us. How satisfying.

[*They sit down, a distinguished couple—reading from left to right, " King, Queen "—on a bench outside the Woodcutter's hut.*]

Queen [*crossly—she was like that*]. I don't know why you dragged me here.

King. As I told you, my love, to be alone.

[*All attendants go off.*]

Queen. Well, you aren't alone.

[*She indicates the Woodcutter.*]

King. Pooh, he doesn't matter. . . . Well now, about these three Princes. They are getting on my mind rather. It is time we decided which one of them is to marry our beloved child. The trouble is to choose between them.

Queen. As regards appetite, there is nothing to choose between them. They are three of the heartiest eaters I have met for some time.

King. You are right. The sooner we choose one of them, and send the other two about their business, the better. [*Reflectively*] There were six peaches on the breakfast-table this morning. Did I get one? No.

Queen. Did *I* get one? No.

King. Did our darling get one—not that it matters? No.

Queen. It is a pity that the seven-headed bull died last year.

King [*with a sigh*]. Those days are over. We must think of a new test. Somehow I think that, in a son-in-law, moral worth is even more to be desired than mere brute strength. Now my suggestion is this: that you should disguise yourself as a beggar woman and approach each of the three Princes in turn, supplicating their charity. In this way we shall discover which of the three has the kindest heart. What do you say, my dear?

Queen. An excellent plan. If you remember, I suggested it myself yesterday.

King [*annoyed*]. Well, of course, it had been in my mind for some time. I don't claim that the idea is original; it has often been done in our family. [*Getting up*] Well then, if you will get ready, my dear, I will go and find our three friends and see that they come this way.

[*They go out together. The music of " Tête à Tête "*

is played again. As soon as they are out of sight the Princess comes back.]

Princess. Well, Woodcutter, what did I tell you ?

Woodcutter. What *did* you tell me ?

Princess. Didn't you listen to what they said ?

Woodcutter. I didn't listen, but I couldn't help hearing.

Princess. Well, *I* couldn't help listening. And unless you stop it somehow, I shall be married to one of them to-night.

Woodcutter. Which one ?

Princess. The one with the kindest heart—whichever that is.

Woodcutter. Supposing they all have kind hearts ?

Princess [*confidently*]. They won't. They never have. In our circles when three Princes come together, one of them has a kind heart and the other two haven't. [*Surprised*] Haven't you read any history at all ?

Woodcutter. I have no time for reading. But I think it's time history was altered a little. We'll alter it this afternoon.

Princess. What do you mean ?

Woodcutter. Leave this to me. I've got an idea.

Princess [*clapping her hands*]. Oh, how clever of you! But what do you want me to do ?

Woodcutter [*pointing*]. You know the glade over there where the brook runs through it ? Wait for me there.

Princess. I obey my lord's commands.

[*She blows him a kiss and runs off.*]

[*The Woodcutter resumes his work. By-and-by the Red Prince comes along. He is a—well, you will see for yourself what he is like.*]

Red Prince. Ah, fellow . . . Fellow! . . . I said fellow ! [*Yes, that sort of man.*]

Woodcutter [*looking up*]. Were you speaking to me, my lord ?

Red Prince. There is no other fellow here that I can see.

[*The Woodcutter looks round to make sure, peers behind a tree or two, and comes back to the Prince.*]

Woodcutter. Yes, you must have meant me.

Red Prince. Yes, of course I meant you, fellow. Have you seen the Princess come past this way? I was told she was waiting for me here.

Woodcutter. She is not here, my lord. [*Looking round to see that they are alone*] My lord, are you one of the Princes who is seeking the hand of the Princess?

Red Prince [*complacently*]. I am, fellow.

Woodcutter. His Majesty the King was here awhile ago. He is to make his decision between you this afternoon. [*Meaningly*] I think I can help you to be the lucky one, my lord.

Red Prince. You suggest that I take an unfair advantage over my fellow-competitors?

Woodcutter. I suggest nothing, my lord. I only say that I can help you.

Red Prince [*magnanimously*]. Well, I will allow you to help me.

Woodcutter. Thank you. Then I will give you this advice. If a beggar woman asks you for a crust of bread this afternoon, remember—it is the test!

Red Prince [*staggered*]. The test! But I haven't *got* a crust of bread!

Woodcutter. Wait here and I will get you one.

[*He goes into the hut.*]

Red Prince [*speaking after him as he goes*]. My good fellow, I am extremely obliged to you, and if ever I can do anything for you, such as returning a crust to you of similar size, or even lending you another slightly smaller one, or—— [*The Woodcutter comes back with the crust*] Ah, thank you, my man, thank you.

Woodcutter. I would suggest, my lord, that you

should take a short walk in this direction [*pointing in the opposite direction to that which the Princess has taken*], and stroll back casually in a few minutes' time when the Queen is here.

Red Prince. Thank you, my man, thank you.

[*He puts the crust in his pocket and goes off.*]

[*The Woodcutter goes on with his work. The Blue Prince comes in and stands watching him in silence for some moments.*]

Woodcutter [*looking up*]. Hullo!

Blue Prince. Hullo!

Woodcutter. What do you want?

Blue Prince. The Princess.

Woodcutter. She's not here.

Blue Prince. Oh!

[*The Woodcutter goes on with his work and the Prince goes on looking at him.*]

Woodcutter [*struck with an idea*]. Are you one of the Princes who is wooing the Princess?

Blue Prince. Yes.

Woodcutter [*coming towards him*]. I believe I could help your Royal Highness.

Blue Prince. Do.

Woodcutter [*doubtfully*]. It would perhaps be not quite fair to the others.

Blue Prince. Don't mind.

Woodcutter. Well then, listen.

[*He pauses a moment and looks round to see that they are alone.*]

Blue Prince. I'm listening.

Woodcutter. If you come back in five minutes, you will see a beggar woman sitting here. She will ask you for a crust of bread. You must give it to her, for it is the way His Majesty has chosen of testing your kindness of heart.

Blue Prince [*feeling in his pocket*]. No bread.

Woodcutter. I will give you some.

Blue Prince. Do.

Woodcutter [*taking a piece from his pocket*]. Here you are.

Blue Prince. Thanks.

Woodcutter. Not at all, I'm very glad to have been able to help you.

[*He goes on with his work. The Blue Prince remains looking at him.*]

Blue Prince [*with a great effort*]. Thanks.

[*He goes slowly away. A moment later the Yellow Prince makes a graceful and languid entry.*]

Yellow Prince. Ah, come hither, my man, come hither.

Woodcutter [*stopping his work and looking up*]. You want me, sir ?

Yellow Prince. Come hither, my man. Tell me, has Her Royal Highness the Princess passed this way lately ?

Woodcutter. The Princess ?

Yellow Prince [*slaps Woodcutter's shoulder*]. Yes, the Princess, my bumpkin. But perhaps you have been too much concerned in your own earthly affairs to have noticed her. You—ah—cut wood, I see.

Woodcutter. Yes, sir, I am a woodcutter.

Yellow Prince. A most absorbing life. Some day we must have a long talk about it. But just now I have other business waiting for me. With your permission, good friend, I will leave you to your fagots.

[*He starts to go.*]

Woodcutter. Beg your pardon, sir, but are you one of those Princes that want to marry our Princess ?

Yellow Prince. I had hoped, good friend, to obtain your permission to do so. I beg you not to refuse it.

Woodcutter. You are making fun of me, sir.

Yellow Prince. Discerning creature.

Woodcutter. All the same, I *can* help you.

Yellow Prince. Then pray do so, log-chopper, and earn my everlasting gratitude.

Woodcutter. The King has decided that whichever of

you three Princes has the kindest heart shall marry his daughter.

Yellow Prince. Then you will be able to bear witness to him that I have already wasted several minutes of my valuable time in condescending to a mere fagot-splitter. Tell him this and the prize is mine. [*Kissing the tips of his fingers*] Princess, I embrace you.

Woodcutter. The King will not listen to me. But if you return here in five minutes, you will find an old woman begging for bread. It is the test which their Majesties have arranged for you. If you share your last crust with her——

Yellow Prince. Yes, but do I look as if I carried a last crust about with me ?

Woodcutter. But see, I will give you one.

Yellow Prince [*taking it between the tips of his fingers*]. Yes, but——

Woodcutter. Put it in your pocket, and when——

Yellow Prince. But, my dear bark-scraper, have you no feeling for clothes at all ? How can I put a thing like this in my pocket ? [*Handing it back to him*] I beg you to wrap it up. Here, take this [*gives him a scarf*]. Neatly, I pray you. [*Taking an orange ribbon out of his pocket*] Perhaps a little of this round it would make it more tolerable. You think so ? I leave it to you. I trust your taste entirely. . . . Leaving a loop for the little finger, I entreat you . . . so. [*He hangs it on his little finger.*] In about five minutes, you said ? We will be there. [*With a bow*] We thank you.

[*He departs delicately. The Woodcutter smiles to himself, puts down his axe and goes off to the Princess. And just in time. For behold ! the King and Queen return. The same music as before. At least we think it is the Queen, but she is so heavily disguised by a cloak which she wears over her Court dress, that for a moment we are not quite sure.*]

King. Now then, my love, if you will sit down on that log there—[*placing her*]—excellent—I think perhaps you should remove the crown. [*Removes it.*] There! Now the disguise is perfect.

Queen. You're sure they are coming? It's a very uncomfortable seat. [*Takes out long nail.*]

King. I told them that the Princess was waiting for them here. Their natural disappointment at finding I was mistaken will make the test of their good-nature an even more exacting one. My own impression is that the Yellow Prince will be the victor.

Queen. Oh, I hate that man.

King [*soothingly*]. Well, well, perhaps it will be the Blue one.

Queen. If anything, I dislike him *more* intensely.

King. Or even the Red.

Queen. Ugh! I can't bear him.

King. Fortunately, dear, you are not called upon to marry any of them. It is for our darling that we are making the great decision. Listen! I hear one coming. I will hide in the cottage and take note of what happens.

[*He disappears into the cottage as the Blue Prince comes in.*]

Queen. Oh, sir, can you kindly spare a crust of bread for a poor old woman! Please, pretty gentleman!

Blue Prince [*standing stolidly in front of her and feeling in his pocket*]. Bread . . . Bread . . . Ah! Bread! [*He offers it.*]

Queen. Oh, thank you, sir. May you be rewarded for your gentle heart.

Blue Prince. Thank you.

[*He stands gazing at her. There is an awkward pause.*]

Queen. A blessing on you, sir.

Blue Prince. Thank you. [*He indicates the crust.*] Bread.

Queen. Ah, you have saved the life of a poor old woman——

Blue Prince. Eat it.

Queen [*embarrassed*]. I—er—you—er——

[*She takes a bite and mumbles something.*]

Blue Prince. What?

Queen [*swallowing with great difficulty*]. I'm almost too happy to eat, sir. Leave a poor old woman alone with her happiness, and——

Blue Prince. Not too happy. Too weak. Help you eat. [*He breaks off a piece and holds it to her mouth. With a great effort the Queen disposes of it.*] Good! . . . Again! [*She does it again.*] Now! [*She swallows another piece.*] Last piece! [*She takes it in. He pats her kindly on the back, and she nearly chokes.*] Good. . . . Better now?

Queen [*weakly*]. Much.

Blue Prince. Good-day.

Queen [*with an effort*]. Good-day, kind gentleman.

[*He goes out.*]

[*The King is just coming from the cottage, when he returns suddenly. The King slips back again.*]

Blue Prince. Small piece left over. [*He gives it to her. She looks hopelessly at him.*] Good-bye.

[*He goes.*]

Queen [*throwing the piece down violently*]. Ugh! What a man!

King [*coming out*]. Well, well, my dear, we have discovered the winner.

Queen [*from the heart*]. Detestable person!

King. The rest of the competition is of course more in the nature of a formality——

Queen. Thank goodness.

King. However, I think that it will prevent unnecessary discussion afterwards if we—— Take care, here is another one. [*He hurries back.*]

[*Enter the Red Prince.*]

Queen [*with not nearly so much conviction*]. Could

you spare a crust of bread, sir, for a poor hungry old woman ?

Red Prince. A crust of bread, madam ? Certainly. As luck will have it, I have a crust on me. My last one, but—your need is greater than mine. Eat, I pray.

Queen. Th-thank you, sir.

Red Prince. Not at all. Come, eat. Let me have the pleasure of seeing you eating.

Queen. M-might I take it home with me, pretty gentleman ?

Red Prince [*firmly*]. No, no. I must see you eating. Come ! I will take no denial.

Queen. Th-thank you, sir. [*Hopefully*] Won't you share it with me ?

Red Prince. No, I insist on your having it all. I am in the mood to be generous. Oblige me by eating it now, for I am in a hurry ; yet I will not go until you have eaten. [*She does her best.*] You eat but slowly. [*Sternly.*] Did you deceive me when you said you were hungry ?

Queen. N-no. I'm very hungry. [*She eats.*]

Red Prince. That's better. Now understand—however poor I am, I can always find a crust of bread for an old woman. Always ! Remember this when next you are hungry. . . . You spoke ? [*She shakes her head and goes on eating.*] Finished ?

Queen [*with great difficulty*]. Yes, thank you, pretty gentleman.

Red Prince. There's a piece on the ground there that you dropped. [*She eats it in dumb agony.*] Finished ?

Queen [*huskily*]. Yes, thank you, pretty gentleman.

Red Prince. Then I will leave you, madam. Good-morning. [*He goes out.*]

[*The Queen rises in fury. The King is about to come out of the cottage, when the Yellow Prince enters. The Queen sits down again and mumbles some-*

thing. It is certainly not an appeal for bread, but the Yellow Prince is not to be denied.]

Yellow Prince [*gallantly*]. My poor woman, you are in distress. It pains me to see it, madam, it pains me terribly. Can it be that you are hungry? I thought so, I thought so. Give me the great pleasure, madam, of relieving your hunger. See [*holding up his finger*], my own poor meal. Take it! It is yours.

Queen [*with difficulty*]. I am not hungry.

Yellow Prince. Ah, madam, I see what it is. You do not wish to deprive me. You tell yourself, perchance, that it is not fitting that one in your station of life should partake of the meals of the highly born. You are not used, you say, to the food of Princes. Your rougher palate——

Queen [*hopefully*]. Did you say the food of Princes?

Yellow Prince. Where was I, madam. You interrupted me. No matter—eat. [*She takes the scarf and unties the ribbon.*] Ah, now I remember. I was saying that your rougher palate——

Queen [*discovering the worst*]. No! no! not bread!

Yellow Prince. Bread, madam, the staff of life. Come, madam, will you not eat? [*She tries desperately.*] What can be more delightful than a crust of bread by the wayside?

[*The Queen shrieks and falls back in a swoon. The King rushes out to her.*]

King [*to Yellow Prince*]. Quick, quick, find the Princess.

Yellow Prince. The Princess—find the Princess!

[*He goes vaguely off and we shall not see him again. But the Woodcutter and the Princess do not need to be found. They are here.*]

Woodcutter [*to Princess*]. Go to her, but don't show that you know me.

[*He goes into the cottage, and the Princess hastens to her father.*]

Princess. Father!

King. Ah, my dear, you're just in time. Your mother——

Princess. My mother?

King. Yes, yes. A little plan of mine—of hers—your poor mother. Dear, dear!

Princess. But what's the matter?

King. She is suffering from a surfeit of bread, and——

[*The Woodcutter comes up with a flagon of wine.*]

Woodcutter. Poor old woman! She has fainted from exhaustion. Let me give her some——

Queen [*shrieking*]. No, no, not bread! I will *not* have any more bread.

Woodcutter. Drink this, my poor woman.

Queen [*opening her eyes*]. Did you say drink?

[*She seizes the flagon and drinks.*]

Princess. Oh, sir, you have saved my mother's life!

Woodcutter. Not at all.

King. I thank you, my man, I thank you.

Queen [*goes to Woodcutter and flings her arms round him*]. My deliverer! Tell me who you are!

Princess. It is my mother, the Queen, who asks you.

Woodcutter [*amazed, as well he may be*]. The Queen!

[*Kneels and covers his face.*]

King. Yes, yes. Certainly, the Queen.

Woodcutter [*taking off his hat*]. Pardon, your Majesty. I am a woodcutter, who lives alone here, far away from courts.

Queen. Well, you've got more sense in your head than any of the Princes that *I've* seen lately. You'd better come to court.

Princess [*shyly*]. You will be very welcome, sir.

Queen. And you'd better marry the Princess.

King. Isn't that perhaps going a *little* too far, dear?

Queen. Well, you wanted kindness of heart in your son-in-law, and you've got it. And he's got common sense too. [*To Woodcutter*] Tell me, what do you think of bread as—as a form of nourishment?

Woodcutter [*cautiously*]. One can have too much of it.

Queen. Exactly my view. [*To King*] There you are, you see.

King. Well, if you insist. The great thing, of course, is that our darling child should be happy.

Princess. I will do my best, father.

[*She takes the Woodcutter's hand.*]

King. Then the marriage will take place this evening. [*With a wave of his wand*] Let the revels begin.

[*They begin. Children dance, the refrain of the "Fairy Story" being used. The King and Queen go off, and the Curtain falls.*]

ROBIN HOOD

By Alfred Noyes

CHARACTERS

Scene I

First Rustic.
Second Rustic.
Robin Hood.
Third Rustic.
The Sheriff.
Will Scarlet.
The Knight.
Rustics and Outlaws.
The Sheriff's Guards.

Scene II

Jenny, *Marian's maid.*
Maid Marian.
Widow Scarlet, *Will's mother.*
Prince John.
Warman, *his man.*
Robin Hood.
The Knight.
Friar Tuck.
Will Scarlet.
Shadow-of-a-Leaf, *a Fool.*
Two servants of Prince John's.
Outlaws.

Sherwood in the twilight, is Robin Hood awake?
Grey and ghostly shadows are gliding through the brake,
Shadows of the dappled deer, dreaming of the morn,
Dreaming of a shadowy man that winds a shadowy horn.

Robin Hood is here again: all his merry thieves
Hear a ghostly bugle-note shivering through the leaves,
Calling as he used to call, faint and far away,
In Sherwood, in Sherwood, about the break of day.

Merry, merry England has kissed the lips of June:
All the wings of fairyland were here beneath the moon,
Like a flight of rose-leaves fluttering in a mist
Of opal and ruby and pearl and amethyst.

Merry, merry England is waking as of old
With eyes of blither hazel and hair of brighter gold:
For Robin Hood is here again beneath the bursting spray
In Sherwood, in Sherwood, about the break of day.

From "Sherwood."

ROBIN HOOD

SCENE I

May-day. An open place (near Nottingham). A crowd of rustics and townsfolk assembling to see the execution of Will Scarlet.

First Rustic. A sad May-day! Where yonder gallows glowers,
We should have raised the May-pole.
Second Rustic. Ay, no songs,
No dancing on the green.
[*Enter Robin Hood, disguised as an old beggar, with a green patch on one eye.*]
Robin. Is this the place,
Masters, where they're agoin' to hang Will Scarlet?
First Rustic. Ay, father, more's the pity.
Robin. Eh, don't ye think
There may be scuffling, masters?
First Rustic. There's many here would swing a cudgel and help
To trip the Sheriff up. If Robin Hood
Were only here!
Third Rustic. They say Prince John is out
This very day, scouring thro' Sherwood Forest,
In quest of Lady Marian!
Robin [*sharply*]. You heard that?
Third Rustic. Ay, for they say she's flown to Sherwood Forest.

Second Rustic. She'd best beware then ; for I saw Prince John !
With these same eyes I saw him riding out
To Sherwood, not an hour ago.

Robin. You saw him ?

Second Rustic. Ay, and he only took three men-at-arms.

First Rustic. Three men-at-arms ! Why, then, he must ha' known
That Robin's men would all be busy here !
I think there'll be some scuffling after all.

Robin. Ay, tell 'em so—go, spread it thro' the crowd ! [*He mutters to himself.*]
He'd take some time to find her, but 'fore God
We must be quick ; 'fore God we must be quick !

Second Rustic. Why, father, one would never think to see thee
Thou hadst so sound a heart.

First Rustic. Ah, here they come !
The Sheriff and his men ; and, in the midst,
There's poor Will Scarlet bound.

The Crowd. Ah, here they come !

First Rustic. There, there he is. His face is white ; but, Lord,
He takes it bravely.

Second Rustic. He's a brave man is Will.

Sheriff. Back with the crowd there, guards ; delay no time !

Some Women in the Crowd. Ah, ah, poor lad !

Robin [*eagerly*]. What are they doing now ?
I cannot see !

First Rustic. The Sheriff's angered now !

Second Rustic. Ay, for they say the hangman has not come.

Third Rustic. The Sheriff says he will not be delayed.
But who will do the hanging then ?

Robin. I have a thought ; make way ; let me bespeak

The Sheriff!

Rustics. How now, father, what's to do?

Robin. Make way, I tell you. I'm the man they want!

Sheriff. What's this?

Robin. Good master Sheriff, I've a grudge
Against Will Scarlet. Let me have the task
Of sending him to heaven!

Crowd. Ah-h-h, the old devil!

Sheriff. Come on, then, and be brief!

Robin. I'm not a hangman;
But I can cleave your thinnest hazel wand
At sixty yards.

Sheriff. Shoot, then, and make an end.
Make way there, clear the way!

[*An opening is made in the crowd. Robin stands in the gap.*]

Crowd. Ah-h-h, the old devil!

Robin. I'll shoot him one on either side, just graze him,
To show you how I love him; then the third
Slick in his heart.

[*He shoots. A murmur goes up from the crowd.*]

Sheriff [*angrily*]. Take care! You've cut the cord
That bound him on that side!

Robin. Then here's the second.
I will be careful. [*He takes a steady aim.*]

A Rustic to his Neighbours. I'faith, lads, he can shoot.

[*Robin shoots. A louder murmur goes up from the crowd.*]

Sheriff. You have cut the rope again!

A Cry. He has cut him free!

Robin. All right! All right! It's only to tease the dog.
Here's for the third now.

[*He aims and shoots quickly. There is a loud cry of a wounded man; then a shout from the crowd.*]

First Rustic. What has he done?

Second Rustic. He has killed
One of the Sheriff's men!

Sheriff. There's treachery here!
I'll cleave the first man's heart that moves!

Robin. Will Scarlet,
Pick up that dead man's dagger!

Sheriff. Treachery! Help!
Down with the villain!

Robin [*throws off his beggar's crouch and hurls the Sheriff and several of his men back amongst the crowd. His cloak drops off.*] Sherwood! A merry Sherwood!

Rustics. Ah, ha! The Lincoln green! A Robin Hood!

[*A bugle rings out and immediately some of the yokels throw off their disguise, and the Lincoln green appears as by magic amongst the crowd. The guards are rushed and hustled by them. Robin and several of his men make a ring round Will Scarlet.*]

Sheriff. It is the outlawed Earl of Huntingdon:
There is a great reward upon his head.
Down with him!

[*The Sheriff's men make a rush at the little band. A knight in jet-black armour, with a red-cross shield, suddenly appears and forces his way through the mob, sword in hand.*]

Knight. What, so many against so few!
Back, you damned wolves. Now, foresters, follow me,
Up, cudgels, for our Saint George, and drive them all
Home to the devil!

[*The foresters make a rush with him, and the Sheriff and his men take to flight.*]

Robin. Now back to Sherwood, swiftly!

[*He sees the Knight in armour standing by his horse.*]

Your pardon, sir; our debt to you is great,
Too great almost for thanks; but if you be

Bound by the vows of chivalry, I pray you
Lend me your charger; and my men will bring you
To my poor home in Sherwood. There you'll find
A most abundant gratitude.

Knight. Your name?

Robin. Was Huntingdon; but now is Robin Hood.

Knight. If I refuse?

Robin. Then, sir, I must perforce
Take him. I am an outlaw, but the law
Of manhood still constrains me. It is a matter
Of life or death.

Knight. Take him and God be with you.
I'll follow you to Sherwood with your men.

[*Robin seizes the horse, leaps to the saddle, and gallops away.*]

SCENE II

Sherwood Forest. Outside the cave, Jenny, Marian, and Widow Scarlet.

Marian. This dreadful waiting! Oh, I am selfish, mother;
You need not be afraid. Robin will bring
Will Scarlet safely back. Jenny, how long
D'you think they've been away. The sun is high,
And all the dew is gone.

Jenny. Now don't you keep a-fretting. They'll be back,
Quite soon enough. [*To Widow Scarlet.*]
Come, widow, come with me.
I'll give you my own corner in the hut
And make you cosy. If you take a nap,
Will Scarlet will be here betimes you wake.

[*Takes her to the hut and shuts her in.*]

There, drat her, for a mumping mumble-crust!
What's that? [*She pauses and stares at the bracken.*]

Marian. Why, Jenny, how you startled me!

Jenny. I thought I saw a face there in the ferns
Yonder—there—see, they are shaking still.
[*She screams.*]
Ah! Ah!

[*Prince John and another man appear advancing across the glade.*]

John. So here's my dainty tigress in her den.

[*At a sign from Marian, Jenny goes quickly inside the cave.*]

That's well! Dismiss your maid!
Warman, remove a little. [*His man retires.*]
I see you think
A little better of me. Out in the wood
There waits a palfrey for you, and the stirrup
Longs, as I long, to clasp your dainty foot.
[*He draws nearer.*]

Marian. Wait—I must think, must think.

John. Give me your hand!
Why do you shrink from me? If you could know
The fire that burns me night and day.

Marian. You are mad!

John. Ay, mad for you.

[*Jenny comes out of the cave and hands Marian a bow. She leaps back and aims it at John.*]

Marian. Back, you wild beast, or by the heaven above us,
I'll kill you! Now, don't doubt me. I can shoot
Truly as any forester. I swear,
Prince or no prince, king or no king, I'll kill you
If you should stir one step from where you stand.

John. I was beside myself, was carried away.
I cannot help my love for——

Marian. I'll not hear
Another sickening word: throw down your arms,
That dagger at your side.

John. Marian, I swear—

Marian. You see that rusty stain

Upon the silver birch down yonder? Watch.

[*She shoots. Then swiftly aims at him again.*]

Now, throw your weapon down.

[*He pulls out the dagger and throws it down, with a shrug of his shoulders. One of his men steals up behind Marian.*]

Jenny. There's one behind you! Look!

[*The man springs forward and seizes Marian's arms.*]

John [*coming forward and taking hold of her also*]. So, my sweet tigress,

You're trapped then, are you? Well, we'll waste no time!

We'll talk this over when we reach the castle.

Keep off the maid, there, Warman; I can manage

This turbulent beauty. Ah, by God, you shall

Come! Ah! God's blood, what's this?

[*Marian has succeeded in drawing her dagger and slightly wounding him. She wrests herself free.*]

Marian. Keep back, I warn you!

John [*advancing slowly*]. Strike, now strike if you will. You will not like

To see the red blood spurting up your hand.

That's not maid's work. Come, strike!

[*Robin Hood appears at the edge of the glade behind him.*]

You see, you cannot!

Your heart is tenderer than you think.

Robin [*quietly*]. Prince John!

John [*turns round and confronts Robin*]. Out with your blade, Warman.

[*Robin draws his sword and sets his back to an oak. The other two followers of Prince John come out of the wood.*]

Robin. Come on, all four!

You must be tired of fighting women-folk.

Come on! By God, sir, you must guard your head

Better than that, [*He disarms Warman.*]

Or you're just food for worms

Already; come, you dogs!

John. Work round, you three,
Behind him! Drive him out from that damned oak!

Robin. Oh, that's a princely speech! Have at you, sir!

[*He strikes Prince John's sword out of his hand, and turns suddenly to confront the others. John picks up a dagger and makes as if to stab Robin in the back. At the same instant bugles are heard in the distance. The red-cross knight flashes between the trees, and seizing John's arm in his gauntleted hand, disarms him, then turns to help Robin.*

Knight. What, four on one! Down with your blades, you curs,
Or, by Mahound!—

[*The three men take to flight. John stands staring at the new-comer. The foresters appear, surrounding the glade.*]

John [*muttering*]. What? Thou? Thou? Or his ghost?
No—no—it cannot be.

Robin. Let them yelp home.
All's well; but take this villain into the cave
And guard him there.

[*The foresters lead Prince John into the cave.*]

John [*to the foresters*]. Answer me one thing; who
Is yonder red-cross knight?

A Forester. No friend of thine,
Whoever he be!

Knight [*to Robin*]. I need not ask *his* name.
I grieve to know it!

Robin. Sir, I am much beholden
To your good chivalry. What thanks is mine
To give is all your own.

Knight. Then I ask this!
Give me that prisoner! I think his life is mine!

Robin. You saved my own, and more, you saved much more
Than my poor life is worth. But, sir, think well
This man is dangerous, not to me alone,
But to the King of England.

Knight. I have more reasons than you know.

Robin. So be it.
Bring back the prisoner!

[*The foresters bring Prince John back. He stares at the knight as if in fear.*]

Sir, you shall judge him.
This prisoner is your own.

Knight. Then—let him go!

Foresters. What! Set him free?

Robin. Obey!

[*They release Prince John.*]

Knight. Out of my sight;
Go!

Prince John. What man is this?

Knight. Quickly, get thee gone!

[*Prince John goes out, shaken and white.*]

Robin. We'll think no more of him! It is our rule
That every friend we meet in merry greenwood
Should dine with us. Will you not be our guest?

Knight. That's a most happy thought! I have not heard
A merrier word than dinner all this day.

Robin. Will you not raise your visor,
And let us know to whose good knightly hand
We are so beholden?

Knight. Sir, you will pardon me
If, for a little, I remain unknown.
But, tell me, are you not that Robin Hood
Who breaks the forest's laws?

Robin. That is my name.
We hold this earth as naturally our own
As the glad common air we breathe. We think
No man, no king, can so usurp the world

As not to give us room to live free lives,
But, if you shrink from eating the King's deer——

Knight. Shrink? Ha! ha! ha! I count it as my own!

[*The foresters appear, preparing the dinner on a table of green turfs beneath a spreading oak. Marian and Jenny appear at the door of the hut. Jenny goes across to help at the preparations for dinner.*]

Robin. Ah, there's my Lady Marian! Will you not come
And speak with her?

[*He and the Knight go and talk to Marian in the background.*]

Little John [*at the table*]. The trenchers all are set;
Manchets of wheat, cream, curds, and honey-cakes,
Venison pasties, roasted pigeons! Much,
Run to the cave; we'll broach our rarest wine
To-day.

[*Enter Friar Tuck with several more foresters and Will Scarlet.*]

Robin. Will Scarlet! And all in time for dinner!
Go into the hut. Thy mother is waiting there.
Put thy big arm around her.

[*Will Scarlet goes into the hut with a cry.*]

Scarlet. Mother!

Friar Tuck. You see,
My sons, you couldn't expect the lad to run!
There is a certain looseness in the limbs,
A quaking of the flesh that overcomes
The bravest who has felt a hangman's rope
Cuddling his neck.

Robin. You judge him by the rope
That cuddles your slim waist! Oh, you sweet armful,
Sit down and pant! I warrant you were glad
To bear him company.

Friar Tuck. I'll not deny it!
I am a man of solids. Like the Church,
I am founded on a rock. [*He sits down.*]

Robin. Solids, i' faith!
Sir, it is true he is partly based on beef;
He grapples with it squarely; but fluids, too,
Have played their part in that cathedral choir
He calls his throat. One godless virtue, sir,
They seem to have given him. Never a nightingale
Gurgles jug! jug! in mellower tones than he
When jugs are flowing. Never a thrush can pipe
Sweet, sweet, so rarely as, when a pipe of wine
Summers his throttle, we'll make him sing to us
One of his heathen ditties—*The Malmsey Butt*,
Or *Down the Merry Red Lane!*

Jenny [*approaching*]. Please you, sirs, all is ready!

Friar Tuck. Ah, Jenny, Jenny, Jenny, that's good news!

[*Will Scarlet comes out of the hut with his arm round his mother. They all sit down at the table of turfs.*]

[*Enter Shadow-of-a-Leaf timidly.*]

Shadow-of-a-Leaf. Is there a place for me?

A Forester. Ay, come along!

Friar Tuck. Now, Robin, don't forget the grace, my son.

Robin [*standing up*]. It is our custom, sir, since our repast
Is borrowed from the King, to drain one cup
To him, and his return from the Crusade,
Before we dine. That same wine-bibbing friar
Calls it our "grace"; and constitutes himself
Remembrancer—without a cause, for never
Have we forgotten, never while bugles ring
Thro' Sherwood, shall forget—Outlaws, the King!

[*All stand up except the Knight.*]

Cries. The King and his return from the Crusade!

[*They drink and resume their seats.*]

Robin. You did not drink the health, sir Knight. I hope
You hold with Lion-heart.

Knight. Yes; I hold with him.

You were too quick for me. I had not drawn
These gauntlets off.
But tell me, Lady Marian,
When is your bridal day with Robin Hood?

Marian. We shall be wedded when the King comes home
From the Crusade.

Knight. Ah, when the King comes home!
That's music—all the birds of April sing
In those four words for me—the King comes home.

Marian. I am glad you love him, sir.

Robin. But you're not eating!
Your helmet's locked and barred. Will you not raise
Your visor?

Knight. Or lose my dinner! Hunger and thirst
Break down all masks and all disguises, Robin.

[*He rises and removes his helmet, revealing the face of Richard Cœur de Lion.*]

Robin. The King! [*They all leap to their feet.*]

Outlaws. The King! The King!

Robin. But oh, my liege,
I should have known, at the rescue of Will Scarlet,
When we were so outnumbered and hard beset,
And you came riding out of the Eastern sky,
I should have known, either it was Saint George
Or else the King come home from the Crusade.

Richard. A lover's instinct might have told you, Robin,
If, as I understand, it means so much
To you and Lady Marian. Huntingdon,
Your earldom we restore to you this day.
You and my Lady Marian shall return
To court with us, where your true bridal troth
Shall be fulfilled with golden marriage bells.
Now, friends, the venison pasty. We must hear
The Malmsey Butt and *Down the Merry Red Lane.*

Shadow-of-a-Leaf. Don't leave the forest. There's darker things to come.

Robin. Pardon him, sire. Poor Shadow-of-a-Leaf has lost
His mortal wits.

Shadow-of-a-Leaf. Sire, you will pardon me,
For I am only a fool, and yet, methinks,
You know not half the meaning of those words—
The King, the King comes home from the Crusade!
Thrust up your swords, hilt uppermost, my lads,
And shout—the King comes home from the Crusade.

[*He leaps on a seat, and thrusts up the King's sword, hilt uppermost, as if it were a cross.*]

CURTAIN

THE SLIPPERS OF CINDERELLA

BY W. GRAHAM ROBERTSON

CHARACTERS

MYRA TREMAINE.
POLLY TREMAINE, } *Twins.*
DOLLY TREMAINE, }
JIMMY TREMAINE.
BELINDA TREMAINE.
AGATHA-NEXT-DOOR.
JANE.
ELIZA.
THE FAIRY GODMOTHER.

THE SLIPPERS OF CINDERELLA

SCENE.—*A very shabby parlour. At back is a curtained window on one side of which stands a bookcase, on the other a grandfather clock stopped at twenty minutes past eleven. A fireplace* R. *with mirror over mantelpiece. Doors* R. *and* L. *Myra, a tall girl of fourteen, sits at a table mending Jimmy's coat while he stands in his shirt-sleeves watching the operation. Belinda sits on a stool by the fire absorbed in a book. The curtains are drawn and the room lit. It is about five o'clock on the 31st of October.*

Myra. There. That's the best I can do with it. Really, Jimmy, any one would think that you walked on your elbows.

Jimmy [*putting on coat*]. Thanks awfully. Does it look very patchy?

Myra. Not so bad. You must try and keep full face when there's company, and sit with your back to the wall.

Jimmy. I don't do much sitting in these knickers; they're at their last gasp.

Myra. I suppose we're a very discontented family. When we had all the nice things we didn't particularly notice them; now we haven't got them we miss them dreadfully.

Jimmy. It's not so much having no nice things as having nasty ones that I object to.

Belinda [*holding out her frock*]. I know. I never cared for this when it was Myra's, and when it was cut up for Dolly I hated it. Now it's mine I simply loathe it.

Jimmy. At any rate you don't run the risk of going off with a bang whenever you sit down.

[*Walks drearily to the window, draws aside curtain and stares into the darkness.*]

What time will the Old Dears be back, Myra?

Myra. I don't quite know; mother said she would telegraph. O Jimmy, I do hope to goodness that father gets this appointment.

Jimmy. Estate agent to Lord What's-his-name, isn't it?

Myra. Yes. What exactly are the duties ot an estate agent, Jimmy?

Jimmy. Oh—you wear riding breeches, you know, and—well, you tell the other fellows to do the rest.

Belinda. I'm sure father could do that beautifully.

Myra. And it would show off his nice legs. I've always recommended the ballet or a bishopric.

Jimmy. I suppose it wouldn't exactly restore the tallen fortunes of our house?

Myra. Not quite, of course, but we should be in the country again, and poor Jane would be able to remember whether she's nurse or parlourmaid or cook. [*Enter* R. *Polly and Dolly in hats and coats. They carry satchels, which they throw down.*] Hullo, Tweenies—late, aren't you?

Polly. Not particularly. It's so dark; there's a fog coming on, I think.

Dolly. A good, thick, yellow one. Ugh. [*Shivers.*] [*The twins take off hats and coats and throw them down.*] And lots of the girls have got parties. It's Hallowe'en, you know.

Belinda. O Dolly—Hallowe'en, when all the fairies are abroad?

Polly. Little silly, with your fairies.

Dolly. What are you stodging over? [*Looking over Belinda's shoulder*] Cinderella, of course.

Myra. Fairies won't come our way, I'm afraid. Now, children, you must clear away all that litter [*pointing to coats*] and then try to get yourselves decently clean.

Twins [*open-mouthed*]. Clean? Whatever for?

Myra. Have you forgotten high tea and Aunt Maria?

Jimmy. I say, Myra—it isn't *this* evening?

Polly. And the Old Dears away, and just us—we, I mean?

Myra. It is—worse luck. She's going to take me to a lecture.

Jimmy. Oughtn't we to have run to dinner for aunt? She's one of the idle rich, you know.

Myra. The lecture's early: besides, I thought high tea rather a good touch; hospitable, yet without the opulence of dinner.

Jimmy. Filling, but not fashionable, eh?

Polly. What's the lecture about?

Myra. Economy.

Dolly. What is economy?

Myra. I believe it teaches you how to spend very little money.

Jimmy. We don't find much difficulty in doing *that.* Now, if it taught you how to spend a great deal of money when you haven't got any, then there'd be sense in it.

Myra. I'm not sure, but I can't help fancying that father looks to Aunt Maria to do that.

Twins. Aunt Maria?

Myra. She's tremendously rich, you know. Simply frightfully. And you see, if she took a fancy to one of us——

Jimmy. Or even two—we could offer the pair of twins at a reduction.

Dolly. Oh, do chuck it, Jimmy. I don't know why there should be anything absurd about being a twin—but there *is.*

Polly. Yes. You needn't rub it in.

Jimmy. Well, unless I'm much mistaken she'll go in for quality, not quantity. A stalwart nephew to support her tottering steps will about fill her bill, I should say.

Myra. Or a sensible, elderly niece who would be a companion to her.

Belinda. Or a dear little girl to brighten her declining—oh, don't, Jimmy.

[*Jimmy shies a cushion at her.*]

Polly. But why Aunt Maria *now* ? She has hardly ever come near us.

Jimmy. She doesn't like us ; and she's only a half aunt really, you know.

Belinda. O Jimmy, how dreadful. Which half ?

Jimmy. Shut up.

Myra. She saw Jimmy and me when we were little and loathed us ; now, I suppose, she's coming back with a fresh eye to see if she likes us any better.

Jimmy [*gloomily*]. She won't.

Myra. No, I don't suppose she will. Of course, from the pathetic point of view, we should have made a better show as orphans.

Dolly. We can't very well work that.

Myra. Hardly, with a brace of parents in robust health on the premises. If we only knew her tastes we could play up better.

Polly. If we each take a different line she may find one of us sympathetic.

Myra. Good idea, Polly. Now—who shall be what ? How about the Tweenies ?

Jimmy. One can be pretty and the other good.

Polly. Bags I being pretty.

Dolly. No, Polly, you're ever so much better than I am. *I'll* be pretty.

Jimmy. Toss up—your call, Polly.

Polly. Heads.

Jimmy [*tossing a penny*]. Tails. Dolly's pretty.

you're good. Then there must be a clever one who swots over lessons—auntie may like that sort—and we ought to have an angel child.

Myra. I'm the clever one, I suppose: that leaves Belinda for the angel child.

Jimmy. Belinda, forward please.

Belinda [*advancing bashfully*]. O Jimmy——

Jimmy [*sternly*]. No back answers. You'll be sitting at the window, your wistful gaze fixed upon the distant hills.

Belinda. You can't see anything but chimney pots from this window—and it's pitch dark.

Jimmy. S-sh. And when she comes in you'll look up with a sad smile.

Myra. Let's try it once over and see how it works out. [*Group formed. Belinda at window, Myra sitting at table, and the twins gracefully posed at her feet.*] I ought to be reading aloud something improving.

Jimmy [*at bookcase*]. Try *Flowering Plants of Great Britain*; some of the words in that are a fair treat. Catch. [*Myra fields a heavy volume with difficulty.*] Now—picture; the Poor but Virtuous Family. H'm-m. Not bad. Why are you making those silly faces, Dolly?

Dolly. I'm looking pretty; you told me to.

Jimmy. Better cut out the prettiness—it would put any aunt off. That's better. Don't grin, Belinda.

Belinda. You told me to. That's the sad smile.

Jimmy. Cut out the sad smile. What utter poops you girls are. You've no more notion of—I say, here *is* somebody! Now then, Myra—and don't look up, any one, when the door opens. Let it all soak in.

Myra [*reading*]. ' In plants of the Umbelliferous Tribe the floral leaves, grown in a whorl and forming what is termed an Involucre, often grow at the base of the general and partial umbels——"

[*Jane appears at door.*]

Jane. If you please, Miss Myra, could I speak to you for a minute?

Myra. Jane! *Not* the kitchen flue?

Jane. No, miss.

Myra. Then I can bear it. What's the matter?

Jane. Nothing, miss, leastways no more than usual; but was you wishful that I should be dressed for the door seeing I'm to dish up the minute your aunt comes and everything so to speak trembling in the balance?

Myra. O Jane, I'm afraid so. Mother made such a point of it.

Jane. Then 'Eaven 'elp the lemon soles, miss, that's all I can say. No, Miss Myra, I can open a door with any one in the land, and I can cook you a sole as wouldn't have disgraced your Pa's table in the Dogwood Park days, but I can't do 'em both at once and keep my reason, and so I tell you.

Myra [*rising, and taking Jane's hand*]. Jane, dear, we must forget the Dogwood Park days. We've all come down in the world now, and you were a dear old silly to come with us.

Jane [*tearfully*]. And do I ever complain, Miss Myra? Do I mind being engaged as a General and doing the work of a Commander-in-Chief? Do I mind sleeping in what you may well call the pantry, for pant you do with a window the size of a sixpence, and arm-in-arm with the boiler—but dress for the door and leave them blessed soles, lemon though they be, and never would Mrs. Silverside have allowed such things to breathe the air ot Dogwood Park while *she* was housekeeper. Well, Miss Myra, we lives and we learns, and *I may* learn to be in two places at once and do a dozen things at the same time—I may or I may *not*, but—— [*Myra looks anxiously at Jane and sniffs suspiciously. Jane sniffs.*] Something burning? There! If I turn my back halt a minute—though I suppose we should reckon it as one of the blessings of living in a rabbit hutch ; what's done in the kitchen you smell in the attic.

[*She dashes from the room.*]

Myra [*laughing*]. Poor, dear Jane. I always smell burning when she gets a little long-winded ; it sends her off like a shot. But now, seriously, children, this is *my* evening, and the important question is—what *am* I to wear ? Mother particularly said that it was to be "quiet and appropriate." What would be appropriate for an Economy Lecture ?

Jimmy. Your oldest frock, or none at all, I should say.

Myra. But you couldn't call that quiet. As a fact, I haven't got anything. Agatha-next-Door offered me the loan of a purple velvet trimmed with swansdown, but I thought *not*.

Dolly. What on earth made you tell *her* about it ?

Jimmy. If there is one thing beastlier than the general beastliness of everything it's the continued patronage of Agatha-next-Door.

Polly. And her habit of "dropping in to play with us," as she puts it.

Dolly. At all hours.

Myra. She's really quite a good sort, and it's nice of her to offer her frocks. The mere fact that one wouldn't be found dead in them ought not to weigh with us. But I *do* wish that I had something decent.

Dolly. What we want is a little woman to come in.

Belinda [*suddenly*]. What we want is a fairy godmother.

All [*in scorn*]. A fairy godmother !

Belinda. Yes, and the Old Dears ought to have seen about it long ago.

Myra. Belinda, you are not to call father and mother the Old Dears. I've told you over and over again.

Belinda. But you and Jimmy—oh !

Jimmy [*shying another cushion*]. Shut it, Belinda.

Myra. All the same there's something in the idea. The fairy godmother would merely wave her wand and there should I be, "quiet and appropriate."

Polly. And a lovely motor to take you to the lecture.

Myra. And a splendid person to open the door in a gold-laced coat and canary-coloured knee-breeches.

Dolly. My dear Myra, Jane would die first.

Myra [*laughing*]. So she would: I forgot Jane. Well, then, a beautiful Greek maiden in flowing raiment and wreathed with roses.

Jimmy. And the high tea. Peacock pasties, haunches of venison, grapes, pineapples—my eye!

Myra. Ah, Jimmy, I'm afraid that fairy days are over. It is not for us poor moderns to stand in the slippers of Cinderella. [*A knock at the door.*]

Polly [*in horror*]. Not aunt? Not yet?

A Voice [*without*]. May I come in?

Jimmy. Worse. Agatha. [*Shouting.*] Oh, come in.

[*Enter Agatha, a very pretty girl, but showily and badly dressed.*]

Agatha. Jane had the door open, so I thought I would just drop in to——

Jimmy. I know. To play with us. We are feeling particularly sportive this evening. Let me introduce Miss Myra Tremaine, the champion Kiss-in-the-Ring player, and Miss Belinda Tremaine, who holds the cup for Hop Scotch.

Myra [*taking Agatha's hand and looking her up and down*]. Dear me, Agatha, another smart frock. You look like a bridesmaid.

Polly. Sorry to disappoint you, but Belinda's engagement to the Archbishop of Canterbury is off.

Dolly. Because she objects to his smoking all over the house.

Agatha [*sinking into a chair and holding out her frock*]. *This* smart? My dear, my maid ran this up for me ages ago: it's as old as the hills and washes like a rag. By the bye, I came upon something that might be useful to you for to-night. I know you're such a one for the quiet shades. It's that very soft tone of pink ; frazy crazy the French call it.

Myra [*puzzled*]. What ? Oh, I see. Fraise écrasée —crushed strawberry. It's ever so kind of you, Agatha dear, but you really mustn't trouble.

Agatha. Trouble's a pleasure, I'm sure. My little maid shall run for it—she's waiting outside. [*Calling*] Faites monter le carton, Elise—tut—stupid of me. It seems so natural to speak to one's fum de chambre in French. [*Calling*] Bring up the box I left in our hall, Elise.

Jimmy. What's your—er—fum de chambre doing here ?

Agatha. She came round with me, of course; mamma would not dream of letting me go out unattended. So you are entertaining this evening ?

Myra. Only Lady Errington.

Agatha [*eagerly*]. Lady Errington ?

Polly. That's Aunt Maria.

Agatha. Lady Errington. Oh—but oughtn't you to smarten up a bit ? With a yard or two of art muslin and a few pins I could make this a different room. Mamma always says I am such a one for the delicate touches. Have you got the right cards to the top in the card plate ?

Dolly. We haven't a card plate.

Polly. And only the sweep's card to put in it if we had.

Agatha. Ah, well, you're new-comers, you see, and perhaps we *are* a little exclusive. How would it be if *I* stayed to dinner so as to give a tone and to show her ladyship that you visit with the *better* houses in the neighbourhood ?

Jimmy. But next door is just like this house.

Agatha [*gently*]. We come at the end of the row, you see, dear. That makes us Semi-detached, doesn't it ?

Myra [*smiling*]. And is that very distinguished? We're dreadfully ignorant.

Agatha. Well, after the Semi you come to the Detached—in gardens—and there you practically touch the County.

Myra. Do you?

Agatha. At any rate the Landed Gentry. [*A knock. Enter a very small child in cap and apron, carrying a large dress box.*] There. Now we'll just have a peep and then you must let Elise get you into it. So much depends upon the way a thing's worn.

Myra. Oh, but—please, Agatha, I couldn't think of troubling—er—Elise.

Agatha. My dear, what has she to do? A little light fancy work——

Eliza [*anxiously*]. Please, miss——

Agatha. A little lace to mend—what is it, Elise?

Eliza. If you please, miss, I was to get back to the potatoes the very minute you'd finished with me.

Agatha [*hastily*]. Open the box at once, Elise. There! [*An appalling garment is disclosed.*] Now, won't that be just the thing? Dressy, you know, and yet only a simple little demi-toilette.

[*Myra gazes in stricken silence, then kisses Agatha.*]

Myra. Thank you, Agatha. It's wonderful. It's—it's wonderful. Isn't it, girls?

Awed Chorus. Quite—quite wonderful.

Myra. And I'm sure it would be *just* right for *some* occasions——

Jimmy [*very politely*]. The Fifth of November, for instance.

Myra. Jimmy! But I'm afraid it's a little too smart for me.

Agatha. Ah, but wait till you see it on. Take the box upstairs, Elise.

[*Agatha opens door* L. *for Eliza, who staggers out with box.*]

Jimmy [*softly*]. Myra, you can't. You'd look like a sweep on May-day.

Myra. Of course I can't, but we mustn't hurt her feelings.

Agatha [*at door*]. Come along, Myra.

Myra [*to Jimmy*]. You come too, and we'll work it somehow.

Agatha [*archly*]. Yes, Mr. Jimmy, you come too and give your opinion. We all know how particular the gentlemen are.

[*Exeunt Myra, Agatha, and Jimmy*, L.]

Polly [*giggling*]. "The gentlemen." Why not "gents"?

Dolly. "There you touch the County."

Belinda [*looking up suddenly from her book*]. Brutes, both of you.

Polly. Brutes?

Belinda. She's nice and kind and pretty, and you're always horrid to her. And Myra told you to clear up the room and wash yourselves.

Polly. Well—I—never.

Dolly. For the first time I realize the feelings of Balaam.

Polly [*severely*]. Belinda clears up the room for sheer, unprovoked cheek.

Dolly [*twitching away Belinda's book*]. Step lively, Belinda.

Belinda [*rising*]. All right. I don't mind. I may as well fag for you as for Jimmy. [*She takes up Polly's coat. Three small objects fall from the pocket.*] Hullo. Chestnuts. [*Picking them up.*] Only three?

Dolly. Hand them over. We'll roast them now—there'll be one each. [*She arranges the three chestnuts on the bars of the grate.*] That's mine, that's Polly's, and that's Belinda's—if she behaves herself.

Polly. One of the girls gave them to me because it's Hallowe'en. I forget why.

Dolly [*kneeling on the rug*]. I know. If your chestnut pops and jumps off the bar you get a wish—your "heart's desire," as some silly book calls it. What's your heart's desire, Polly.

Polly [*with a sigh*]. I couldn't possibly stuff 'em into one chestnut; I've got so many.

Dolly [*clearing the fire with the poker*]. So have I. And of course it *is* all nonsense: Jane might just as well expect to get her heart's desire from a lemon sole.

Belinda. Dolly, you mustn't talk like that on Hallowe'en. It's the great fairy night, and I'm sure we *ought* to wish.

Polly. Well, there's your chestnut. Wish away and see what your fairies can do for you.

Belinda [*with closed eyes and tightly clenched hands*]. Then I wish—oh, I *do* wish—that a fairy godmother would appear and give us *all* our wishes. Why shouldn't she come to us as well as to Cinderella? *She* only wanted to go to a silly ball; *we* want such lots of things. [*The room darkens and a loud pop is heard.*]

Polly. There goes a chestnut. Whose is it?

Dolly [*raking among the ashes*]. Belinda's, I think. What's wrong with the light? I can hardly see.

Belinda. It *is* mine. O Polly, you—you don't *really* think that anything's going to happen, do you? I almost wish that we *hadn't* wished.

[*The room darkens still more, leaving only the dull glow of the fire.*]

Dolly [*looking nervously round*]. Don't be absurd, child. It's—it's some stupid trick of Jimmy's, I expect.

[*A sound of music is heard; soft, rippling arpeggios which seem to come from immense distance.*]

Polly [*loudly*]. Stop it, Jimmy. We're not a bit frightened. [*Clinging to Dolly.*] O—oh, Dolly.

[*The music sounds nearer and now voices can be heard, faint but shrill, blent in a wild, wordless chant. The three children huddle together on the hearth-rug.*]

Dolly. O—oh—look there.

[*Out of the darkness grows a pale silvery light. The window curtains wave as if in a strong gale, then sweep aside disclosing the tiny, shining figure of the Fairy. She wears a long red robe and a steeple-crowned hat; her little face is that of a child, but long grey hair flows over her shoulders, and she leans upon a crutch of ebony. She peers into the room with drowsy eyes while the music sinks to a whisper, then ceases.*]

Fairy [*in a faint, far-away voice*]. Who calls upon the Name Forgotten? Who wakes the Faerie from their dream?

Belinda. We—we didn't know you were asleep. We're *so* sorry.

Fairy. What should we do but sleep in a world which knows us no longer? My eyes are grown dim. [*She draws from her robe and puts on a huge pair of horn spectacles.*] Are you not my little Cinderella?

Belinda. Please—I'm Belinda, please.

Fairy [*peering at her*]. I know not Belinda. But [*passing her hand over her brows*] I have slumbered long. [*Her eyes fall upon the prostrate twins.*] And these—these should be your sisters. [*Shaking her crutch with a menacing gesture.*] Ugly and cruel, doubtless.

Belinda [*hastily*]. Yes, they're my sisters, but they aren't ugly—at least, not particularly—and they're quite nice.

Twins [*piteously*]. Oh, we *are*—we really *are*, dear Fairy: quite.

Fairy. Then what ails the child? Has the king, your father, brought you home a cruel stepmother?

Polly. Mother is quite well, thank you.

Dolly. And father isn't a king.

Fairy. Strange. Strange. Then perchance he is a poor woodcutter?

Belinda. He's poor, but he isn't a woodcutter.

Polly. He wants to be an estate agent.

Fairy. I know not the estate agent. Is it a noble calling?

Dolly. They look after land, I think.

Fairy. Ah, the Governor of a Province. A modest ambition truly, and he shall attain it. [*She waves her crutch.*] He is an estate agent from henceforth. [*To Belinda.*] And now for you, my child. What boon would you ask of the Faerie?

Belinda [*overcoming her nervousness and advancing a few steps*]. Oh, dear Fairy, it isn't for me—it's for Myra.

Fairy. Myra?

Belinda. She's my eldest sister, you know.

Fairy. The Princess Royal? Yes.

Belinda. She's going out to-night with Aunt Maria, and she hasn't a single decent frock.

Fairy. Is she good and true, this Myra?

Belinda. She's a perfect dear.

Dolly. Everybody likes Myra.

Fairy. Then to-night she shall be fairest of the fair. Shall hers be the robe that blazes like the sun, that shines like the moon, or that glitters like the stars?

Polly. I think—if you wouldn't mind—something a little quieter.

Dolly. Yes, she said " quiet and appropriate."

Fairy. Modest and wise Myra. White shall be her raiment; white as the Dawn before the Sun has kissed her. What more?

Belinda. Well—if she *could* have something to take her to the hall.

Polly. A taxi, you know——

Dolly. Or even the station fly——

Fairy. A suitable equipage. Good.

Belinda. Then—what was it she wanted for poor Jane?

Polly. A neat gown to open the door in.

Fairy. A bower maiden in fair apparel. Yes.

But you have then bidden guests hither? I will transform this hovel to halls of splendour.

[*Raises her crutch.*]

Dolly [*hastily*]. No, no, please. You mustn't. This is a furnished house—and we mayn't transform anything.

Polly. They won't even let us shift the bookcase.

Fairy. Then at least I will provide a banquet.

Belinda [*doubtfully*]. We've got lemon soles.

Polly. Of course, a cold chicken *would* be nice.

Fairy [*sharply*]. Tut, tut. Leave that to me, child.

Polly. I beg your pardon, dear Fairy—and we're ever so much obliged. Now Agatha-Next-Door won't be able to wave her frightful frocks at Myra any more.

Fairy. What is this malapert Agatha that she should taunt the Lady Myra? Shall I cause toads to fall from her lips with her every word?

Belinda. Oh no, *please* don't.

Polly [*regretfully*]. Perhaps it would be better not. She never leaves off talking, so the place would be *full* of toads.

Dolly. And she doesn't exactly taunt, you know, only she has such heaps of frocks and there's Myra without one to her back.

Fairy. This at least shall be remedied.

[*She describes a circle round herself in the air with her crutch, then with arms uplifted, she chants.*]

This to That and That to This,
One shall find what one shall miss:
Black to white and white to black,
This shall gain what That shall lack;
This shall lose what That shall hold
Till the strokes of twelve be told—a—ah!

[*As she speaks the last line she totters as if faint.*]

Children. Oh, what is it? Aren't you well?

[*The Fairy recovers herself and stands leaning on her crutch, but her speech is faint and breathless.*]

Fairy. I have spoken no Spell this many a day. Now the Great Words come slowly to my lips and my feet falter on the Ancient Way. I am weary, my children: let me go.

[*The brightness about her begins to fade.*]

Polly. We are so sorry that you should have tired yourself for us.

Dolly. But, dear Fairy, why are you so old and weak? I thought that Fairies were always young and dancing in the moonbeams.

[*The far-away music sounds again as the Fairy answers slowly.*]

Fairy. We are the world's first babies, dear; the children of its youth and innocence: now it grows grim and overwise and cares to play with us no longer. It is falling—falling, the twilight of the fairies: soon the midsummer moon will look on us no more.

[*There is now only a pale glimmer of light round the little figure.*]

Polly. Oh—she's going.

Dolly. She's putting herself out.

Belinda [*darting forward*]. One minute, please, Fairy! Must Myra be careful about twelve o'clock—like Cinderella, you know?

[*Through the shadows the last words of the Fairy fall faintly.*]

Fairy. This shall lose what That shall hold
Till the strokes of twelve be told.

[*Complete darkness. The music once more swells to a chorus of wild voices, then dies away to a mere breath—the sigh of an Æolian harp. Suddenly the room flashes again into brightness: the normal atmosphere has again returned, the window curtains are closed, and the Fairy has vanished.*]

Belinda. "Till the strokes of twelve be told." That means till twelve o'clock, doesn't it?

Polly [*dreamily*]. I—suppose so.

Belinda. They'll be home long before that, but I'm

glad I remembered to ask. Aunt Maria would be dreadfully annoyed to find herself bouncing down High Street in a pumpkin.

Polly [*suddenly*]. Dolly—pinch me. Harder. I *can't* be awake.

Dolly. Polly—then it really did happen ? It's true ?

Polly. The—the Fairy ? I—suppose so.

Belinda [*clapping her hands and skipping*]. Of course it's true, and we've got all these nice things for Myra. A fly to take her to the lecture——

Polly. A cold chicken—that was *my* idea.

Belinda. A new frock.

Dolly. I suppose the—[*looking nervously over her shoulder*] the old lady knows the sort of thing that girls wear now ?

Polly. She said " white " : you can't go far wrong with plain white. When will this Spell affair begin to work ?

Dolly. Don't talk as if it were a mustard poultice. Almost at once, I should think. I wonder that we haven't heard cries of joy already.

Polly. S'sh. Listen.

[*A distant commotion is heard, voices raised in alarm, the upsetting of chairs, a door violently slammed. Hurried footsteps draw near, and Eliza bursts in* L. *and dashes across to the opposite door. She is pale and breathless.*]

Dolly and Belinda. What is it ?

Polly [*between Eliza and the door* R.]. What's the matter ?

Eliza [*wildly*]. Don't you stop me !—I wouldn't stay another minute in this house, not—not if it was *ever* so. Don't you stop me, Miss Polly !

[*She slips past Polly and out* R. *As the children stare at each other the front door is heard to bang.*]

Dolly. Can anything be wrong upstairs ?

Polly. Perhaps I'd better go and see.

Dolly. Wait—here comes some one else. Agatha !

[*Agatha runs in* L., *a terrified and dishevelled Agatha, dressed only in her bodice and petticoat. Her hair, freed from ribbons and combs, falls over her shoulders; all her affectations have vanished; she is a pretty and pathetic little figure.*]

Agatha [*in a choked voice*]. Girls—I—I didn't leave my clothes down here, did I?

Polly. Clothes? Of course not.

Dolly. What on earth has happened?

Agatha. I—I don't know. Oh, poor Myra! [*Covering her face with her hands.*] I believe I'm going out of my mind.

Dolly [*severely*]. You've gone out of quite enough already, seems to me. Where's your frock?

Agatha. I—I don't know.

Polly. Don't *know*?

Agatha [*wildly.*] Oh, don't ask questions or I shall scream! Who's that? [*The door* L. *bursts open and Jimmy runs in. Agatha rushes to him.*] Jimmy. Is she any better?

Jimmy [*panting*]. Worse. It's awful. Why did you cut away?

Agatha. I couldn't stand it—when she began to sprout.

Children. *Sprout*? Myra? What's she sprouting?

Jimmy. It looks like feathers.

Children. *Feathers*?

Jimmy. And now her tail's growing—there are yards and yards of it on the floor.

Children. Her *tail*?

Agatha [*faintly*]. Oh, don't! Jimmy—couldn't you run for the doctor?

Jimmy. I suppose I'd better: Dr. Raynor at the corner?

Agatha. No, no, he's homœopathic: I'm sure she wants violent treatment. Dr. Bargrave in Milford Street.

Jimmy. Right-o. [*Turning to twins.*] And you

girls standing there like gaping geese, why don't you *do* something? Take her up a cup of tea—or a hot water bottle—or *something*.

Myra [*without*]. Jimmy. Jimmy.

Polly. Hush. I believe she's coming.

[*Belinda runs to door* L. *and flings it open*.]

Belinda [*staring in ecstacy*]. O Myra! How lovely!

Jimmy. O Myra! How awful!

All. O my good gracious goodness, Myra!!

[*Myra totters in, supporting herself from chair to chair, until she reaches the table, against which she leans trembling. A beam of fairy radiance falls upon her, emphasizing the glories of her toilette. She is in full evening dress of white satin with a heavy court train falling from the shoulders, and embroidered with pearl and diamond flowers. Diamonds blaze at her throat and on her corsage, ropes of pearls hang from her neck, and her arms and fingers are loaded with bracelets and rings. On her head is a diamond tiara, from which waves a forest of white ostrich plumes.*]

Myra. Jimmy—how could you leave me, Jimmy?

Jimmy. I'm going for the doctor.

Myra [*clutching him*]. No, no. Let's all keep together. I don't know what may be going to happen next.

Agatha. I don't know what has happened *now*. I can't understand.

Myra. Well—you *saw*. I was just trying on that frock of yours when all of a sudden it—it went.

Twins. *Went*?

Myra. It wasn't there. And then *her* frock went—and then I began to break out like this. Don't come near me, children; it's probably catching.

Agatha. O Myra, the jewels! I shouldn't mind catching some of them. *Look* at the diamonds—and aren't those pearls—pearls as big as marbles?

Jimmy. And they're stuck all over her. My word,

if we could spout her as she stands she'd fetch pounds and pounds.

Agatha. Pounds? That dress is worth hundreds—thousands!

Myra. But it won't come off—I've tried. Not a thing will come off.

Jimmy [*aghast*]. Won't come off? But it *must.* You can't go about like that. I'll tell you plainly you don't come tagging after me down town in white satin and feathers.

Belinda [*solemnly*]. It will all vanish at twelve o'clock, just like Cinderella's ball dress.

Jimmy. Oh, shut your head, Belinda.

Myra. Look here, Belinda, we've got enough to worry us without *your* twaddle. Don't talk of what you know nothing about.

Polly. But she *does* know.

Dolly. She's trying to tell you. It's true.

Myra. One at a time, children. *What's* true?

Jimmy. Come on, cough it up, Belinda.

Belinda. True that a Fairy came and——

Myra. A *what*?

Polly. A Fairy.

Dolly. Yes, really a Fairy. We saw her too.

Belinda. It's Hallowe'en, you know. She gave us all wishes, and I wanted you to have a nice new frock for the Economy Lecture.

Myra. And—is this it?

Jimmy [*going into guffaws of laughter*]. Oh, my eye, the Economy Lecture! Quiet and appropriate—eh, Myra?

Belinda. We said it was to be quiet and appropriate, didn't we?

Twins. Yes, yes, we did.

Myra [*with the calm of despair*]. I should like to see the Fairy's notion of something a little dressy. But what about poor Agatha? Is your Fairy responsible for *her* present—er—costume?

Agatha [*ruefully*]. It seems to be all or nothing with her.

Belinda. That was Polly.

Polly. Sneak. I may have hinted that Agatha had too many frocks, but I never asked the old lady to take away every stitch the girl stands up in.

Dolly. How were we to know that fairies are so beastly literal ?

Jimmy [*taking off his coat*]. I call it a shame. Here, Agatha, put this on. It won't look quite so—so evening dress. [*Helps Agatha into the coat.*]

Myra. Well, there's only one thing to be done. Polly must go to the lecture, Agatha must go to bed, and I must shut myself into the boot cupboard until twelve o'clock. Now I hope this is all, Belinda—no more wishes.

Belinda. No.

Dolly [*feebly*]. N-no—except Jane.

Polly. And the cold chicken.

[*A loud crash is heard as of breaking crockery.*]

Myra. Belinda—that wretched Fairy isn't starting on *Jane* now—when you know as well as I do how the least thing upsets her ?

Children. But we only asked——

Jane [*without*]. If you please, miss—— [*The door* R. *is kicked violently open and Jane staggers in bearing upon a silver dish a monstrous gilded pasty from which emerge the head and tail of a well-grown peacock. Jane is attired in flowing robes of pale almond pink, and decked with gold bracelets and a necklet of gold coins ; on her head is a wreath of pink roses entwined with golden leaves.*] If you please, Miss Myra, was it by your orders that *this* was sent in ? [*She slams down the pasty on the table and stands gazing at it as though fascinated.*] When I see the creature staring at me it give me such a turn I dropped a pile o' plates—and never would your Ma approve of any such French fallals and kickshaws from the pastrycook, Miss Myra ;

"If you please, miss, was it by your orders that this was sent in?"

plain roast and boiled was good enough for Dogwood Park and—— [*Her glance falls upon Agatha.*] Lor, Miss Agatha! [*Realizing Myra.*] Sakes alive, Miss Myra!

Chorus. Jane!

Jane. Ah, Jane indeed. No, Miss Myra, it's not my place to pass remarks, and none shall be passed: I merely ask you whether *this* is what your Ma would have ordered for high tea for six, let alone the hares and pheasants, shot in like coals they were, and there's a whole stag in the passage and two swans in the sink.

Myra [*hopelessly*]. It's quite useless to explain. A —a friend has sent us a little present of game, Jane.

Jane. Then there's been some mistake in delivery, you mark my words; it's the Lord Mayor's Banquet we've got, Miss Myra, and our brace o' rabbits has gone to the Mansion House.

Belinda. O Jane, you do look lovely.

Jimmy [*struggling with laughter*]. I say, Jane, have you seen yourself lately?

Jane. Seen myself, Master Jimmy? Ah, some of us *ought* to see ourselves—you standing there a disgrace in your shirt-sleeves and Miss Agatha dressed —well, I won't say how—and as to Miss Myra, it's not for me to pass remarks, but her Ma wouldn't like it, no more her aunt won't neither. *My* tastes was always quiet, thanks be; plain washin' print for week days and a nice bit o' black for Sunday——

Myra. Jane, dear—I think you had better take a look at yourself.

Jane. Me, Miss Myra? Is my cap crooked? [*Raising her hands to her wreath.*] Why—what's all this? [*Seeing her gold clasped arms.*] Oh! [*She cautiously approaches the mirror above the mantelpiece and takes one glance at it.*] Oh! [*She sinks into a chair by the table.*] What is it, Miss Myra? What's done it? Oh—oh, it's crool. Dressed for the door I was by your Ma's wish, and now [*extending her bare arms*] I might be going to do the week's washing.

[*Flings her arms along the table, buries her face in them and sobs.*]

Myra. Now she's going into hysterics. I hope you're satisfied, Belinda.

Jimmy. Yes, Belinda, you and your footling Fairy have got us into a rotten mess between you.

Polly. Don't speak of her like that, Jimmy.

Dolly. You might remember that she could turn us all into white rats or guinea pigs.

Myra [*wildly*]. I'd *rather* be a guinea pig. I shouldn't feel nearly such a f-fool as a guinea pig.

[*Drops into chair opposite Jane and hides her face on the table. A fanfare of trumpets. Myra and Jane simultaneously raise their heads.*]

Myra and Jane. What's that ?

Jimmy. It sounded just outside.

Agatha [*running to the window and peeping out*]. Good gracious, look !

[*She draws the curtains, the street is seen to be brilliantly lit up. Shouts are heard and a distant hum of voices.*]

Jimmy [*running to the window*]. I say ! Look at those chaps with torches—linkmen don't they call them ? [*The three children run to the window.*]

Agatha. And here come outriders in crimson and silver and—O Myra, do look—[*A louder flourish of trumpets. The shouts and uproar increase*]—*look* at this coming round the corner—[*Jane jumps up and runs to the window*]—six milk-white horses with postilions in cloth of silver and—oh, my goodness—[*Trumpets and an outburst of cheering*]—*such* a coach, all gold and crystal, and as big as a haystack.

Jane. It's the Free Foresters' Feet.

Jimmy. It's the King and Queen.

Belinda [*dancing with excitement*]. No, it isn't. It's the suitable equipage. Wait a minute—there. [*A thunderous knock at the front door.*] It's the carriage come for Myra.

Myra [*faintly*]. I knew it. The Fairy has done things thoroughly.

Dolly. And we only asked for the station fly.

A Tremendous Voice [*from the street*]. THE PRINCESS MYRA'S CARRIAGE STOPS THE WAY.

Jimmy. Stops the way—I should think it *did*: it's the size of a brewer's van.

The Voice. THE PRINCESS MYRA'S CARRIAGE.

Myra. If that creature keeps on bawling out my name I shall go silly.

A Man's Voice [*in the crowd*]. Cheers for the Princess Myra. Hip-hip-hip—— [*A burst of cheering.*]

Agatha. Myra—you'll have to come to the window and bow. Royalties always do.

Myra. No, no. I can't—I won't.

Jimmy [*at window*]. Myra, you jolly well *must*. They're packed like sardines in the street. Come on.

Twins. Yes, come on, Myra.

[*They drag the reluctant Myra to the window.*]

Jimmy. Coat, Agatha, quick. [*Agatha snatches off coat and helps Jimmy into it. Jimmy flings up the sash of window. Loud cheers.*] Ladies and Gentlemen, [*dead silence*] Her Royal Highness the Princess Myra has graciously consented to appear.

[*Bows elaborately. Trumpets. Roars of applause, amidst which Myra steps to the window and bows gravely right and left. She then slams down the sash and draws the curtains quickly. The hubbub sinks to a continuous murmur.*]

Myra [*leaning exhausted against the curtains*]. Will any one kindly tell me what we're going to do *now*?

Jimmy [*scratching his head*]. *I* don't know. And aunt may blow in at any minute.

Polly. Perhaps she won't notice anything.

Jimmy. Perhaps not—with a full-fledged circus at

the door and Jane looking like the "Last Days of Pompeii."

[*Enter Eliza* R. *hastily. At sight of Myra she hesitates and makes for the door again.*]

Eliza. Please, miss——

Myra. What's the matter, Eliza? Don't be frightened.

Eliza. Oh, if you please, miss—missus's compliments, and Miss Agatha's to come home this very minute.

Agatha. I can't, Eliza, you must see that I can't.

Eliza [*with increasing nervousness*]. And please, miss, Number Fifteen desires '*is* compliments and—and——

Myra [*coming towards her*]. Yes? And what?

Eliza [*desperately*]. And 'e's gone for the P'LICE.

[*Dashes from the room.*]

Children. The police.

Jane. The *police*!

Jimmy. That about puts the lid on.

Myra [*calmly*]. Yes. I think we may regard the police as the finishing touch.

Jimmy. Let's see. Five minutes to the station, five minutes back—— [*Agatha glances at the clock.*] That clock's no good: it has been at twenty past eleven ever since we came here. We've got about ten minutes. What's to be done?

Myra [*advancing with tragic dignity*]. I have quite decided what is to be done. I am the eldest and therefore responsible; if the police arrive I shall give myself up—"go quiet" I believe is the expression. You, Polly, will take my place as hostess. Jane, it is too late for the soles; you had better serve that dreadful bird [*pointing to peacock*], but for goodness' sake let it be carved off the table. And you, children, at the height of your high tea, think of your unhappy sister sitting in white satin and diamonds in the police station, and [*almost breaking down*] don't make greater fools of yourselves than is absolutely necessary. [*She passes slowly out* L. *with hanging head.*]

Jimmy. She's handing out the sob stuff pretty thick, isn't she?

Agatha. I think it is very affecting: it's like Mary Queen of Scots going to execution.

Jimmy. Of course we can't let her get jugged. Now—what price medal for distinguished service? Jane, will you lead the forlorn hope—run down and tell those chaps with the coach to go away?

Agatha. Yes. Say it's the wrong house—they've mistaken the day—anything.

Jane. What! *me,* Master Jimmy? Not like this?

Jimmy. Slip on mother's mackintosh.

Agatha. Put up an umbrella. And if the police come——

Jimmy [*wildly*]. If the police come, just give the whole bally show in charge. That ought to keep them busy for a bit.

Jane [*picking up the great dish*]. If the police come I shall give 'em *this*: that's the way to keep 'em busy. Don't you worry, Master Jimmy: I'll see what I can do.

Twins. And we'll come with you, Jane.

[*Exeunt* R. *Jane with the pasty, Polly and Dolly.*]

Jimmy [*stopping Belinda*]. Not you, Belinda; I want a word with you. [*Slaps Agatha on the back.*] Good old Agatha. Still sticking to the ship, eh?

Agatha. Of course; but when the policemen come I shall nip behind those curtains; I'm not—er—dressed to receive.

Jimmy. Then you'd better nip: they'll be here directly. [*Agatha hides behind the window curtains.*] Now, Belinda.

[*Belinda advances timidly, her hands behind her.*]

Belinda. Yes, Jimmy.

Jimmy [*sternly*]. You're at the bottom of all this, you know.

Belinda. Jimmy, I will not be bullied. I've got any amount of people their heart's desire, and if they don't like it, it's not my fault.

Jimmy. But d'you mean to say that this variety entertainment of yours is going to last till midnight ?

Belinda. Yes, till twelve o'clock. The Fairy told me so.

Jimmy. Are you sure ?

Agatha [*poking her head out between the curtains*]. Repeat what she said.

Belinda. It was all in poetry ; I can't remember.

Jimmy [*catching her by the shoulders and shaking her*]. But you must. Think, you little ass, think.

Belinda [*in gasps*]. I—can only—remember—the last two lines. She said them twice.

Jimmy [*releasing her*]. Well—let's have 'em.

Belinda. "This shall—shall——" Oh yes. "This shall lose what That shall hold——"

Jimmy. This shall lose——

Agatha. That's me. That's all right. Goodness knows I've lost enough.

Jimmy. —what That shall hold. That's Myra, I suppose : she's got away with the goods. Go on, child.

Belinda. "Till the strokes of twelve be told."

Jimmy [*hopelessly*]. Till twelve o'clock. That's plain enough. That does us in.

Agatha [*eagerly*]. Well, but, Jimmy, *does* it ? She didn't exactly say till twelve o'clock ; she said, "Until the clock strikes twelve."

Jimmy [*staring at the clock*]. By Jove ! I believe you've hit upon the weak spot. [*The trumpets begin to sound again.*] Oh, shut your heads ! I'll make the clock strike twelve in half a jiff.

[*Jumps on a chair, opens the clock face and seizes the minute hand.*]

Agatha. No, no, Jimmy, not yet ! I'm frightened. It may start something else off—do wait a minute.

Jimmy. What for ?

Agatha. Let's think—let's consult——

Jimmy. If we don't look slippy we shall do our consulting in the station. [*A loud ring, followed by a knock at the front door.*] There ! The police. Agatha, it's now or never. Risk it ?

Agatha [*nodding*]. Risk it.

[*Her head disappears within the curtains. Jimmy whirls the minute hand round to the hour and the clock slowly strikes twelve. As the last stroke falls all sounds from the street cease.*]

Jimmy [*breathlessly*]. Well ?

Agatha. The street is all dark again, and—Jimmy—I can't see the coach : I believe it has gone away.

Jimmy. Let's have a look. [*Draws the curtains, showing Agatha dressed as at first.*] Why—yes. The whole show has done a bunk. The street's quite empty and—[*seeing Agatha*]—hullo !

Agatha. And here's my frock ! Jimmy—it worked. O Jimmy ! [*Embraces him violently.*]

Jimmy [*struggling*]. Here, I say—drop it.

[*The twins rush in* R.]

Dolly. Jimmy, Jimmy ! Jane has come right again.

Polly. And we couldn't find the coach—it's not there.

Jimmy. Good business. My word, what a narrow squeak. Now then for the police—let 'em all come !

Dolly. The police ?

Jimmy. They rang just now. Didn't you let them in ?

Polly. That wasn't the police : it was this telegram for Myra. [*Holds up a telegram.*]

Jimmy [*taking it*]. Give it here.

Myra bursts in L. *Her fairy robes have disappeared, and she is dressed as before.*]

Myra. Look. Look at me ! I'm all right again ! What has happened ?

Jimmy [*solemnly*]. The clock has struck twelve.

All the Girls [*after a pause*]. Oh—oh—you clever boy! [*They all rush at him.*]

Jimmy. Now, drop it, drop it. It was Agatha's idea. Myra, here's a telegram for you.

Myra [*tearing it open and reading.*] "All settled, home this evening. Dad, Mother." Children—he has got it. Dad has really got the appointment.

Jimmy. Well played, the governor.

Twins. Hip, hurray!

Belinda. Of course he has. The Fairy said most particularly——

Jimmy. Oh, *hop* it, Belinda.

Myra. Belinda—if you so much as mention that Fairy again I'll—I'll slap you.

Agatha. Listen. Isn't that a taxi stopping?

Jimmy. Aunt, you bet. Agatha, you must stay to tea. I say, Myra, don't you rather wish you hadn't been shorn of all your splendour?

Myra. Not a bit. I wouldn't stand in Cinderella's shoes again for anything you liked to offer. Yes, here comes aunt.

Jimmy. Now, girls, pull yourselves together. 'Tention! Fall in behind there.

[*Buttons his coat and shoots his cuffs. The girls arrange their frocks and pat their hair. Enter Jane in neat black dress, white cap, and apron.*]

Jane. Lady Errington.

All [*advancing with outstretched hands.*] How d'you do, Aunt Maria?

QUICK CURTAIN

THE DISCOVERY

By Hermon Ould

EDITOR'S PREFACE

The first voyage made by Christopher Columbus across the Atlantic Ocean was one of the most daring and romantic adventures ever undertaken by man. Strong in his faith that by sailing westward from the coast of Europe he would reach the coast of Asia, he overcame all difficulties, and on Friday, August 3, 1492, *he set sail from Palos, in Spain, with three little ships. First he touched at the Canary Islands, and then he launched out into the unknown seas which for centuries had been regarded as the end of the world. We can hardly imagine him worse equipped. His own ship, the " Santa Maria," the largest of the three and the only one which was completely decked, was about thirty-two yards long and nine yards wide. Many of his men were criminals released to join the expedition because so few sailors would venture, and there was hardly a man on the three ships who did not dislike Columbus as a foreigner and despise or fear him as a madman. Day after day the easterly winds drove them steadily across the ocean, till they grew afraid that they would never be able to return, and discontent and superstition were on the verge of breaking out into mutiny. Still Columbus held to his westward course, but on October* 11 *he knew that if land were not sighted very soon, his crew would murder him, seize the ship, and turn back to Spain.*

CHARACTERS

CHRISTOPHER COLUMBUS.
PEDRO GUTIERREZ, *an officer.*
PEPE, *a page-boy.*
JUAN PATIÑO,
DIEGO GARCIA,
FRANCISCO,
GUILLERMO IRES, } *other seamen.*

Note.—Christopher Columbus first saw the light of the New World on the night of October 11, 1492. He was often "at open defiance" with his crew. These two circumstances, at least, are historical. For the rest, this little play had better be regarded as a work of imagination—H.O.

APPROXIMATE PRONUNCIATIONS

PEDRO GUTIERREZ—*Páy-dro Goo-tee-érreth.*
PEPE—*Páy-pay.*
JUAN PATIÑO—*Hoo-áhn Pah-tée-nyo.*
DIEGO GARCIA—*Dee-áy-go Gar-thée-ah.*
FRANCISCO—*Frahn-thís-co.*
GUILLERMO IRES—*Gill-yáir-mo Êe-rays.*

None of the Spanish vowels is exactly the same as the English. The *e* is something between *ay* in *pay* and *e* in *egg*. The *r* is always rolled. *Th* as in *think*. *G* as in *good*.

Columbus's Spanish name is *Christobal Colon,* but as no one calls him by name in the play, this is not needed.

THE DISCOVERY

SCENE.—*On board the "Santa Maria."*
TIME.—*October* 11, 1492.

The ship is seen from an angle, which brings the poop somewhat to the left, the quarter-deck taking up the greater part of the stage. If it is visible, the midmast should bear a crucifix, in passing which everybody mechanically crosses himself. A large lantern, containing a lighted candle, is fixed at the extreme top of the poop. The night is still, and there is little movement in the sails.

Two seamen are visible, both well to the right. Juan is on his knees, adjusting rigging; Diego is helping. The actions of both of them are indeterminate, clearly designed to conceal their real purpose. They speak in loud whispers.

Diego. Within the next half an hour he will go to the poop-head as sure as God's alive. He can't keep away from it. His eyes are glued on the sky as if he expected his precious New World to burst out of it like a thunderbolt ! [*He laughs derisively.*]

Juan. Poor wretch !

Diego. Now, then, Juan—quaking again !

Juan. That's a lie ! Why should I quake ? What is there to fear ? [*After a brief pause*] But I am sorry for him.

Diego. Why waste your pity ? Shall it be one madman, his head stocked with visions, or forty honest seamen pining for their homes ?

Juan. Santisima Maria, but he's a *gracious* madman . . .

Diego [*impatiently*]. Gracious when all goes to his pleasure, but as irritable as a teething child when crossed!

[*The song of seamen is heard: it is a scarcely distinguishable murmur.*]

Here's a keg o' rum
To Kingdom Come!
The Devil laughs,
But God is dumb!

Juan [*sharply*]. They ought to stop that. The captain is always furious when he hears it.

Diego. Shan't we even *sing* to keep up our spirits? 'Sh!

[*They attend with assumed assiduity to the rigging. Pedro Gutierrez comes in; he is somewhat surprised when he sees the others.*]

Pedro. Who's that?

Diego [*rising*]. Diego Garcia and Juan Patiño, sir.

Pedro [*inclined to be communicative*]. It's dark. I would welcome the moon. . . .

Diego. Aye, aye, Don Pedro. Some of us would welcome the coast of Spain still more.

Pedro [*pumping*]. Impatient, Diego?

Diego [*surlily*]. There are limits to patience, sir.

Pedro [*humouring him*]. And you've reached them, eh?

Diego. We're like bats trying to fly by day. It's time he gave way. Why should one man have the lives of fifty in his hands?

Pedro [*with authority*]. I hope we are not entertaining mutinous thoughts, Diego.

Diego. Mutiny is an ugly word, sir.

Pedro. And an uglier deed.

[*Juan, finishing his job at the rigging, rises, and with a salute goes off. Columbus comes on. He is a tall, well-built man of forty-six. Hair prematurely white, complexion fair, almost ruddy. A man of quick temper and irritability which he controls only with an effort. His face, in repose, is melancholy. Seeing Don Pedro in conversation with Diego, he looks a trifle suspicious. He turns quickly to Diego.*]

Columbus. That candle on the foremast is guttering ; see that it is put right.

Diego [*sullenly*]. Aye, aye, sir. [*He goes.*]

Columbus [*recalling him*]. And, Diego !

Diego [*coming back*]. Yes. sir.

Columbus. This is the quarter-deck.

Diego. Yes, sir.

Columbus. A good sailor knows his place.

Diego [*with repressed fury*]. Yes, sir.

[*Columbus points off ; Diego, scarcely concealing a scowl, goes off.*]

Columbus [*to Pedro*]. A surly dog !

Pedro. And a dangerous one. He does more than his share to inspire discontent.

Columbus. I have remarked it.

[*Columbus is thoughtful for a moment and remains stationary. Presently he goes on to the poop and looks out to sea. Pedro follows him. Simultaneously, Pepe, the page-boy, emerges from the hatchway, against which he stands, out of sight of the others. When they begin to talk he listens eagerly.*]

Columbus. Easterly, ever easterly. God is in the wind, Don Pedro.

Pedro [*with a short laugh*]. The crew would say that it is the Devil, rather, captain. All day, and every day, the wind blows easterly, blowing them away from their homes and their country, their wives and children, their friends and sweethearts.

Columbus [*hastily*]. You too, Don Pedro ? Do you, too, doubt ?

Pedro. Have I said so, captain? Am I not here by your side, prepared?

Columbus. Forgive me, friend. You are one of the few with faith, and it is not easy to hold fast to faith when nothing seems to warrant faith. Listen to that.

Seamen [*off, singing*]:

> Here's a keg o' rum
> To Kingdom Come!
> The Devil laughs,
> But God is dumb!

[*Columbus and Pedro descend to the quarter-deck.*]

Columbus. *Madre de Dios,* they drink too much.

Pedro. They are simple men and must have their relaxation. [*The next words break from him almost involuntarily.*] We have not all your vision, captain.

Columbus. You *are* beginning to doubt, Don Pedro. Give me the contents of your mind. I am an impatient man and prone to be unjust; but—[*whimsically*]—I mean well, Don Pedro. I mean well. Speak without fear.

Pedro [*at first with diffidence, but rapidly gaining confidence*]. To-day is the 11th of October—more than two months since we saw the shores of Spain receding. You held a glittering hope of discovery before us, and we had faith. Day followed day, and soon we found ourselves in uncharted seas, but still we had faith. . . . I, at least, had faith. [*With dignity*] I am a man of some little learning, not easily led to wonder at natural phenomena as the unlettered might be. But I confess that I knew some uneasiness when the needle of the compass, instead of pointing to the constant North, jumped as if the devil had laid hand on it, and pointed to the North-west. I am not a child, nor a simpleton, nor a superstitious seaman; but there is such a thing as being too clever, prying into mysteries which were not meant for our eyes. In all humility, captain, I ask if it is

God's will that we should pursue this voyage in the face of every portent of ill-luck ?

Columbus [*impatiently*]. It is *my* will. Is that not enough ?

Pedro [*bowing his head*]. I am answered.

Columbus [*hastily*]. Forgive me, Don Pedro. A curb for my tongue—oh, a curb for my unbridled tongue, my worst enemy! [*More quietly*] *My* will, friend, because God's will. Shall that suffice ?

Pedro [*not appeased*]. I do not claim your confidence, sir.

Columbus [*thundering again*]. But I claim yours. [*The sound of the seamen's song is again heard.*] A blight upon their singing! Bid them stop. [*Pedro goes off, with an air of discontent. When he is alone, Columbus looks out at sea. Muttering.*] Mystery? Would God implant the desire to solve mysteries and not provide the solution? [*Suddenly Pepe runs up the steps to the poop. Columbus is startled.*] *Pañeta!* Who is that ?

Pepe. Me, captain—Pepe!

Columbus [*frowning on him*]. Have you been there all the time ?

Pepe. Please, sir, I am off duty.

Columbus. Then why aren't you down below ?

Pepe [*whimsically, knowing that he is privileged*]. I prefer your company to theirs. [*He points below.*] Am I in the way here, sir ?

Columbus [*humouring him*]. What a boy! And what do *they* say of the preference ?

Pepe. I don't speak to them. I hate them.

Columbus. 'Sh, Pepe! And get you gone! [*Pepe turns reluctantly.*] Quick! [*The boy goes more quickly.*] Here! You heard what Don Pedro said ?

Pepe. Yes, captain. And *he* is the best . . .

Columbus. But even he doubts . . .

Pepe. Everybody doubts . . . except me.

Columbus [*bitterly*]. Everybody . . .

Pepe [*eagerly*]. Except me, captain, except me.

[*He goes to him impetuously.*]

Columbus [*laying a hand on the boy's head*]. You are young enough to have faith. Thank you, boy.

[*The seamen's song is heard again.*]

Pepe. They are horrible when they drink too much. They say it makes them forget.

Columbus. Poor fellows!

Pepe [*approaching nearer*]. Captain, be careful! Sometimes they are desperate.

[*The song surges up like a growl.*]

Columbus. That is ugly. I bade Don Pedro stop them. So you think they might become dangerous? [*Don Pedro returns.*] Go, boy. [*Pepe moves away, but does not go out.*] Well, Don Pedro? Their singing changes to a roar. The deepening of their discontent is ominous. [*The noise grows louder.*]

Pedro. Captain, they ignore my order.

Columbus [*furious*]. I'll make an example of one of them. [*Suddenly.*] Hallo, there! What sneaking mischief-maker is that crawling about the deck? Show yourself! [*Francisco appears from the right.*]

Columbus. Ho, Francisco—you, is it?

Francisco. Yes, sir. And I'm no sneaking mischief-maker.

Columbus. Then why behave as one? Why are you here? Did I send for you? Is discipline obsolete in the Ocean Sea? Is Jack as good as his master nowadays?

Francisco [*humbly*]. Your words sting, sir!

Columbus. And are meant to. I am tired of the mumbling and grumbling of the crew. I have been patient too long.

Francisco. I came to warn you, sir. The temper of the crew is dangerous.

Columbus. Danger is the breath of my life. I should doubt I lived if I lived outside danger.

Francisco [*the words springing from him spasmodi-*

cally]. Our power of endurance has gone. We refuse to go on. I warn you. I respect your person and do not wish to see violence used ; but it is more than mortal can bear, this endless sailing into unknown seas.

Columbus [*to Pedro*]. Don Pedro, the ship is in your hands. I will talk to our friend as man to man. [*Pedro goes on to the poop. Columbus, his voice gentler, almost ingratiating, turns to Francisco, who shifts from foot to foot, nervous by reason of the unaccustomed propinquity.*] Francisco, let me plead with you. There are men whom God has chosen for the working of His will. I am such a man. There is no more merit in me than in this ship : we are both instruments of God. Sometimes He chooses oddly : a stronger than I might have served His purpose better. But since God chose me, who shall withstand me ? The four corners of the earth are to be linked up in the knowledge of their Saviour. I have lifted the veils which obscured the prophecies of Holy Writ, and I have learned that it was ordained that I, chosen among all men, should discover that great world beyond the ocean which I know exists as surely as I know that Heaven exists.

Francisco. Must simple men suffer because of *your* knowledge ?

Columbus [*quickly*]. Simple men shall do their duty.

Francisco. There are limits to duty. Men will give up many things for duty and for gain, but you ask too much. Country, family, friends, perhaps even life itself—all these things you ask us to give up for *your* glory. *We* are not chosen of God to open up new ways : we are simple, humble men, sick for our homes and hungry for our wives.

Columbus. My Heaven, Francisco, you try me . . .

Francisco [*gaining courage*]. Not more than you try us, sir. I come to you as a friend, sir. The men are at the end of their patience and spoiling for a fight. The stoutest rope breaks at last. [*The song swells up again. Spoken words mingle with the song, and the voice of Guillermo Ires is heard above the rest.*] Did you hear that, sir!

Columbus. I heard the snarling of angry beasts.

Francisco. You heard the just complaints of angry men, sir. [*Again Guillermo's voice pierces the din. Columbus stands rigid, endeavouring to catch the words.*] Did you hear *that*, sir?

Pepe [*who has been unobserved*]. They shan't! They shan't!

Columbus. Boy, come here. What were the words?

Pepe [*almost weeping*]. He said: "The *Santa Maria* will be the lighter for his carcass."

Columbus [*bitterly*]. He said that, did he?

[*He blinks—is moved more than he will show.*]

Francisco. I am sorry, sir. . . . I knew how high feeling had run.

Columbus [*authoritatively*]. Send Guillermo Ires to me!

Francisco [*not without diffidence*]. Sorry, sir, but . . .

Columbus. Discipline knows no buts.

Francisco [*angrily*]. Discipline is a thing of the past, sir. It's you or us.

Columbus [*to Don Pedro*]. Don Pedro, let Guillermo Ires be sent to me. He shall know what it is like in irons.

[*Pedro is half-way down the stairs to the quarter-deck when Guillermo Ires and other seamen rush in an angry mass towards Columbus, growling like infuriated animals.*]

Columbus [*in a thunderous voice*]. Stop! What is the meaning of this wild uproar? [*The men stand transfixed.*] The first man to move shall spend the rest of the night in irons!

[*There is a perceptible pause, during which nobody moves. Then, with a wild cry, Guillermo Ires breaks away from the others and advances towards Columbus.*]

Guillermo. And who's to put him in irons? We are thirty to one.

Columbus [*calmly*]. If nobody else is available for the office, I will perform it myself. Get below! Let me hear no more of this.

Guillermo [*in high excitement*]. We've stood too much. We've been duped day in, day out. We're men with the common feelings of men. We want our homes and our women. I say the *Santa Maria* shall turn her helm towards Spain at once, or we are not men but sheep.

Columbus [*still calm*]. And who shall navigate her?

Guillermo. There's plenty here who can do that. The Devil's with *you*, we all know that, riding the easterly wind; but we are not men unused to the sea. Once clear of this Devil's track to nowhere, we'll blow our way back to home.

[*Signs of assent from the rest of the crew. Columbus raises his hand, appealing for silence. He is paler than his wont, but very calm.*]

Columbus. Don Guillermo, you are an excellent sailor, a man of abundant resourcefulness. Some day, if your tongue does not run away with your discretion, you will achieve prosperity in your calling. To-day you are an able-bodied seaman and no more: I am your captain. Your duty is to obey me as mine is to obey the Royal Sovereigns of Spain who sent me. Let that be clearly understood between us and we shall not fall out. Now return to your duties.

[*Again a perceptible pause. Columbus's authoritative manner holds them. Presently Diego breaks out.*]

Diego. Words for children! Froth and scum! We are men: reason with us!

Columbus. Silence!

[*The tone of authority calms the men, who remain, however, in a huddled crowd, murmuring dis-*

contentedly. Columbus turns and goes up the stairs to the poop, where he stands and look down upon the men.]

Diego [*snarling*]. I suppose you think you're on holy ground now? [*He bounds towards the stairs.*]

Voices [*tumultuously*]. Have him down! Pitch him overboard! Put *him* in irons! Devil's tool! Italian renegade!

[*They are about to stampede up the poop gangway, when Pepe runs to the foot of the stairs and stands with his arms spread out.*]

Pepe. Cowards! Cowards! You will have to kill *me* first!

Voices. Out of the way! Devil's whelp! Lick-spittle!

Columbus. What! Does that child stand between me and death? [*Silence follows the commencement of his speech.*] Pepe! Come here!

Pepe [*going to him quickly*]. My captain!

[*The men are somewhat sheepish.*]

Columbus. Pepe! This is a voyage of discovery. [*The men growl.*] I set out to discover a new world, a radiant land beyond unknown seas; to find new wealth and dominion for our Sovereign King and Queen, new souls for the sacrifice of our Saviour to redeem. So far I have discovered but one thing. [*He pauses and continues with slow deliberation.*] I have discovered that when a man is given a vision he must follow it alone. Loyalty passes like seaweed on an outgoing tide. Friendship breaks as a mast hollowed by worms breaks. Discipline, duty, and honourable obedience are bubbles that burst at the first contact. There remains but oneself. That is my only discovery so far, Pepe.

Pepe [*his eyes gleaming with excitement*]. Captain, *I* am loyal, I am still obedient, still your devoted servant. . . .

Columbus [*with some emotion*]. I am not ungrateful.

Pedro [*scraping his throat, with dignity*]. I hope my loyalty has never been in question, sir?

[*He salutes.*]

Columbus [*returning the salute*]. You have sometimes been silent, Don Pedro, when speech would have made your loyalty clear. But I thank you. . . .

[*Columbus turns and looks out at sea: for a moment his attention is fixed. He peers more earnestly into the darkness. There is a movement among the men. He turns.*]

Juan. We are simple men, sir. . . .

Columbus [*hastily*]. Shall simple men judge their betters?

Guillermo [*surlily*]. We may as well wait till to-morrow, at any rate.

Columbus. Dark deeds are better done in the dark.

[*Guillermo, scowling, but sheepish, slinks off, followed by one or two of the seamen.*]

Francisco. Desperate men do not always act up to the best that is in them, sir.

Columbus [*with quiet irony*]. I thank you for reminding me, Francisco. Your best cannot be bettered. Good-night!

[*Francisco half-turns to speak again, but thinks better of it and goes, shamefaced. Several others go, too, sheepish. A brief silence. Columbus does not move; he is struggling with overwrought emotion. When he speaks his voice is not steady.*]

Columbus. Go, boy!

[*Pepe seizes his hand, kisses it, and hastily descends to the quarter-deck and goes out.*]

Columbus [*turning to Pedro*]. Two minutes ago, Don Pedro, I saw . . . I thought I saw . . [*He peers into the darkness.*] It was . . . It is . . .

Pedro [*in excitement*]. What, sir?

Columbus. A light, faintly flickering, rising up and down. Look! [*He points.*]

Pedro. It *is*, sir! Glory be to God!

[*At this moment there is a wild shout, off.*]

Voice [*off*]. A light! A light! Land! Land!

[*A sailor comes running on, delirious with joy and excitement.*]

Sailor. Did you see it, sir? A light! Blessed Mother of God! A light!

Columbus [*with quiet authority*]. Give the order to heave to.

CURTAIN

ELDORADO

By Bernard Gilbert

EDITOR'S PREFACE

When Spanish and English seamen were sailing westward ho! in search of wealth and great adventure, Eldorado was a magical word. It was the Spanish name for a City of Gold, fabled to be hidden in the forests of South America, and so many men sought for it in vain that it has become proverbial for any dream of great wealth.

In this play, " Eldorado," robbed of its romance, is the name of a seed-potato, which was so much in demand at the height of an extraordinary potato-boom that farmers gave amazing prices for it, certain that it would make their fortunes—and found that it did not.

CHARACTERS

JAMES WATSON, *a farmer ; age* 59.
HENRY WATSON, *his son ; age* 20.
BETSY WATSON, *his daughter ; age* 18.
EMMA BURROWS, *a widow, and market gardener ; age* 52.

The play takes place in a disused windmill, occupied by the Watsons as a farmhouse, in the village of Carrington.

ELDORADO

EXTRACT FROM COUNTY DIRECTORY

CARRINGTON, a village at the foot of the Wolds (476 inhabitants) on the river Sow. The principal landowners are Lord David Herries of Herries Hall, and James Watson, Esquire. Church—St. Peter. Vicar—Rev. W. Martin. Wesleyan Chapel. " The Case is Altered " Inn (James Garvey). " The Nelson Arms " (B. Snow). Railway Station—Belton Junction. Carrington Wood is noted for its primroses. Three great moors—Caxton, Carrington, and Worlby meet here.

The curtain rises one fine March morning on the combined sitting- and dining-room of Jim Watson's farmhouse in the village of Carrington. It doesn't look much like a farmhouse, because it happens to be the bottom storey of a disused windmill. The mill is a very substantial circular brick building, quite sixty feet high. Its ground floor is raised above the yard outside to the height of a wagon bottom, and when the outer door (which is in the centre at the back) is opened, a fine view is obtained across Caxton Moor to where Keal Hill rears its head several miles away. The floor of the living-room is of boards, and so is the ceiling, which is supported by stout beams, from which hang an oil lamp, a fine ham, bunches of dried herbs, and strings of onions. The circular brick wall is whitewashed, presenting a rough appearance, and the only attempts at ornament are a couple of the highly coloured almanacs given away by country tradesmen. Light is obtained from two windows placed high up ; one on the extreme left, the other half-

way round on the right. Their deep ledges draw attention to the great thickness of the wall. Between the front door and the left-hand window is a smaller door, opening into a shed (once a stable) which serves as kitchen and scullery. Between the right-hand window and the front door, a step-ladder, close to the wall, leads to a trap-door in the ceiling. A stout rope hangs from a hook beside this trap. A clumsy deal table stands in the centre of the floor, with a chair drawn up on its left. Under the windows two large wooden bins have been converted into cupboards, and wooden shoots run from the top of these to the ceiling. A mill-stone lying on the floor on the extreme right serves as the base of an iron stove, whose pipe passes through the wall just under the ceiling. An armchair occupies a square of coco-nut matting by the stove, and two plain wooden chairs stand on either side of the scullery door. On one of these is a small lidded egg-basket. A square piece of zinc is nailed to the floor in front of the scullery door, and exactly over this is a second trap-door with two flaps, through a hole in the centre of which hangs an endless chain reaching nearly to the floor. The front door is a very stout affair, with long iron hinge-plates, an iron bar, and a latch. On the extreme left, a shaft with pulley wheels is fixed to the wall.

A melancholy whistling is heard outside, and a young man, coming up the steps to the front door, enters the room and goes to the stove. Henry Watson is a well-built fellow of about twenty, wearing a Norfolk jacket, tweed breeches, and cycling stockings. As he stands holding his hands out over the top of the stove, a high-pitched querulous voice comes from above.

Voice. Is that you, Henry?

Henry. Yes, dad.

[*A creaking of hinges is heard, the right-hand trap-door is raised, and James Watson, grasping the rope, descends the ladder backwards. He is a small, thin man, in tight cloth trousers, with a tightly-fitting coat of snuff-coloured cloth which he wears buttoned up to his chin. His grizzled beard is short and straggly, and his scanty moustache reveals a mean upper lip. The half-top hat he is wearing may have been black when it was fashionable a generation earlier, but is now green with age. His eyes are small and close together, and his whole appearance is mean and withered.*]

James. Well—did you tell 'em what I said?

Henry. Yes.

James. And what did they say?

Henry [*laughing shortly*]. Said as they never expected nothing else.

James. Oh, they did, did they! The bone idle rackapelts! Beer! Beer! Do they think I've got Jackstraw's brewery in the mill-yard? Here I've found 'em a whole gallon—amongst six of 'em, mind you—nearly a quart apiece—only three days ago, and now they want more! If they'd turn teetotal and wear blue ribbons, instead of deafening me with their yauping for beer, I should think something of 'em. Did you tell 'em they could fill their bottles with cold tea?

Henry. Ay! I said I'd take it to them!

James. Were they thankful? What did they say?

Henry [*grinning*]. I don't hardly like to repeat it.

James. Out with it.

Henry. They said you wasn't named "Cheap Jim" for nothing.

James. The shucky mawkins! If they come and beg on their bended knees for cold tea, they shan't have it now—not a drop! I'll dock their wages!

Henry. Then they'll go away and we shan't get our potatoes planted.

Mawkins, Used of ugly or unpleasant people. (All the dialect words are Lincolnshire.)

James. As soon as we're a bit slacker, I will!

Henry. You can't cut 'em down any more, dad. We've only got the oldest hands now—what nobody else won't have. It takes 'em most of their time to draw their breath, and they hoe that careful you can see the weeds grown up behind 'em almost as thick as they are in front.

James. Young chaps is no use. If you get a good 'un, he won't stop; and if you get a bad 'un, you don't want him. In my young days we never had no trouble at all. They were pleased to earn fifteen pence a day, and would very near go down on their knees for it. Nowadays they want us to go down on our knees to get them.

Henry [*interrupting him*]. Tom Harrod came back with me from the field, to fetch another bag of superphosphate. He knows where it is, in the shed—oh yes, and they want another fork!

James [*anxiously*]. They use that manure as if it was sand. What do they think I'm made of!

Henry. If we don't put manure *in* the ground, we shan't get any crop *out.* This isn't fen land.

James. They use too much. I'll tell him they must be more careful. [*He makes towards the front door.*]

Henry [*stopping him*]. What about that fork?

James. Fetch one from the top—the one with the cracked shaft.

[*Henry goes up the steps and disappears through the trap-door. Fainter bangs record his ascent to the fourth story. As James reaches the front door, the scullery door opens and his daughter Betsy hurries out and stops him.*]

Betsy. I haven't got any potatoes for dinner.

James [*trying to get away from her*]. Well, get some.

Betsy. I'm not going through that mucky yard any more. Why can't we have a bag of eaters kept up here, same as you promised.

James. All right! I'll see to it.

[*He breaks loose and runs down the steps into the mill yard.*]

Betsy [*calling from the top of the steps*]. I'm waiting for them!

[*She comes inside, shuts the door, and goes to the stove to make the fire up. Betsy Watson is an obstreperous lass of eighteen, with a keen (and constantly outraged) sense of justice. She wears black hand-knitted stockings, a very old and torn tartan skirt, a spotted blue and white blouse, and down-at-heel black walking shoes, whose broken laces are mended with twine. She has on a dirty white apron, and her sleeves are rolled up. Her mass of straight dark-brown hair is thrown on to the top of her head to be secured there by two or three hair-pins. Under favourable circumstances Betsy would be a good-looking girl, but constant nagging by her father has made her sullen.*

There is a knock on the door, and Betsy, wiping her hands on her apron, goes to open it. The Watsons' next-door neighbour, Widow Burrows, stands on the doorstep.]

Mrs. Burrows. Is your father at home, Betsy?

Betsy [*in a pleased tone*]. Why, Mrs. Burrows! Come inside.

[*Emma Burrows carries on the market gardening business of her late husband Nathan, with the help of her two sons, Joe and Abel. She is a biggish woman of over fifty, with iron-grey hair, humorous hazel eyes, dark rather bushy eyebrows, and a moustache. She wears a black bonnet, trimmed with beads, a full black mantle, heavy with jet trimmings, and a very full black skirt which would sweep the floor but for the fact that she has pinned it up in several places with safety pins, thus displaying her stout elastic-sided boots. She has clearly put on her best clothes to pay a call.*]

Mrs. Burrows [*looking round with intense interest*].

I've never been in since your dad made this into a house.

Betsy. I'm ashamed for anybody to come in, Mrs. Burrows—mind that chain! What mother would have said to us living in a broken-down windmill, when that great Manor House belongs to us, I don't know.

Mrs. Burrows. And your poor mother such a strict Methodist! It's enough to make her turn in her grave to have the *parson* living in *her* house. You'd think they'd build a decent vicarage.

Betsy. Dad's made a laughing-stock of us. The boys shout after me when I go into the village.

Mrs. Burrows. When the sails was blown down in that great storm, folks did reckon as your father would be too mean to put 'em up again, specially as there's another mill so near—but nobody dreamt as he'd come to *live* in it. After all, though, it's a deal more comfortable than I'd have thought. [*She puts her head into the outhouse.*] And this is your scullery, is it?

Betsy [*sulkily*]. And kitchen as well. I'm nearly blown away with the draughts in there.

Mrs. Burrows [*returning*]. I suppose you sleep in the room over this?

Betsy [*sarcastically*]. Oh no! That's the best and driest floor, and so it's packed with potatoes.

Mrs. Burrows. Potatoes! Good gracious! Well, I'm glad your dad's got some left, because that's what I came to see him about.

Betsy. We've any amount. They're stored up in bags and hampers and chitting-boxes: that's why we've got a fire. *I* might starve on the coldest day if it wasn't for *them.*

Mrs. Burrows. Where do you sleep, then?

Betsy. Dad and Henry have the room over the

Chitting-boxes, Boxes in which potatoes are put to sprout in a dark place. *Starve,* Die (of cold).

potatoes, and I'm in the one over that, and then there's one full of apples, and tools, and such-like. The top's empty, 'coz the roof's all broken in.

Mrs. Burrows. You must get a good view up there.

Betsy. I can see Kyme Castle and Sildyke Church on a fine day. They say you can see Barkston, but I never have.

Mrs. Burrows. I should be afraid of rats in a place like this!

Betsy. Oh, bless you, we keep a dog on purpose to catch them. He has to earn his keep, does Jack.

[*The front door is opened, and James Watson returns. Betsy hastily retreats to the scullery and shuts her door.*]

Mrs. Burrows. Good-morning, Mr. Watson.

James. Good-morning, Mrs. Burrows. Sit you down. How are things going with you now?

Mrs. Burrows. Middling! You know what a struggle I've had since Nathan died. If it hadn't been for brother-in-law Japhet coming over from Kyme now and again, I don't know how I should have managed.

James. Anybody 'ud be pleased to help you, Mrs. Burrows.

Mrs. Burrows. Then why didn't you lend me a horse and cart last week, when I was stuck fast?

James [*earnestly*]. I would have done in a minute, only we couldn't manage it. I haven't nearly enough horses.

Mrs. Burrows. You should get more, then.

James. They eat so much. When it rains, they stand in the stable eating and eating, without ever stopping to take breath. I can't bear to see 'em. Every champ costs me a ha'penny.

Mrs. Burrows [*sarcastically*]. I wonder you don't give 'em less.

James. I do, as far as I dare, but the brutes only eat their bedding and nag the mangers.

Mrs. Burrows [*coming to business*]. What I came to see you about, Mr. Watson, was for a bag of your Early Rose potatoes. You've got some, haven't you?

James. Only a few. They're awful scarce this year.

Mrs. Burrows. I saw yours when they was growing. A rare nice patch they looked.

[*Henry comes down the steps with the fork, and hurries out, with a nod to Mrs. Burrows.*]

James. They're shy yielders, them Early Rose. Almost grown out, they are, like all potatoes as lives too long. Why! I can remember 'em when I was a lad only so high. [*He puts his hand near the floor.*] They're nearly all gone now—all them good old sorts—Magnum Bonum, Beauty of Hebron, Myatt's Ash-leaf—beautiful potatoes they was, floury and as sweet as butter.

Mrs. Burrows [*impatiently*]. Yes, yes. But can I have a bag of your Early Roses? They come before anything else in my garden.

James. I don't think you'll get any, anywhere.

Mrs. Burrows. Why?

James. They're so scarce. Tim Williamson of Fletton asked me at Bly Market last Saturday if I had any. He let out that there was very few about, and they're going to a famine price.

Mrs. Burrows. What! He told you that when he was trying to buy some?

James [*scornfully*]. Of course not! That was after I told him I hadn't any to spare.

Mrs. Burrows. Oh, I see! But I only want one bag. You'll let me have that.

James. I'm afraid I can't.

Mrs. Burrows. That's only a dodge to put the price up. Come on! What's the figure?

James. I really can't spare 'em.

Mrs. Burrows. Unless I pay three times what they're worth?

James. You'll not do that, Mrs. Burrows; you're the closest buyer for miles round Carrington.

Mrs. Burrows. And you're the hardest seller this side the Gulland. How much?

James [*suddenly turning serious and speaking slowly*]. Very well, then! I'll let you have a bag as a great favour, being as you're a neighbour and a widow.

Mrs. Burrows. How much?

James. That'll be all right. Leave the price to me. I shan't hurt you.

Mrs. Burrows. I shan't let you. What's the price?

James. Twelve shillings.

Mrs. Burrows. Twelve shillings a bag! Rubbish!

James. That's it, anyhow.

Mrs. Burrows. I shall never pay it.

James. Just as you like. Business is business. You want my potatoes—then you'll have to pay my price for 'em.

[*Henry enters from the yard, and stands by the scullery door, waiting until the old man is free. He plays idly with the endless chain.*]

Mrs. Burrows. I guessed what was up when you wanted me to leave the price. Heaven help anybody as did that! [*Rising.*] Keep your Early Roses. I'll chit some of my Duke of Yorks instead.

James [*imperturbably*]. As you like, missis.

Mrs. Burrows. I'll get brother-in-law Japhet to send me a bag.

James. The carriage'll kill 'em.

Mrs. Burrows. I'd as leave pay the money to the railway as to you, you old skinflint.

Henry [*picking up his cue*]. We haven't many bags of Early Roses left, dad.

James. I thought not!

Mrs. Burrows. Then keep 'em.

James [*as she reaches the door*]. I'll knock you threepence off.

Chit, Sprout (so that they will grow more rapidly when planted).

Mrs. Burrows. Now you're getting rash! But I won't rob you. Brother-in-law Japhet will send me some. It isn't long since he sent a couple of pounds of some new-fangled sort for me to try.

Henry. What was they called, Mrs. Burrows?

Mrs. Burrows. Elderberry.

Henry. Elderberry?

Mrs. Burrows. It was Elder something—either bush or berry. I've got it! Fennell's Elderberry! Brother-in-law Japhet often sends me odd things down as he gets to try. Good-day, Mr. Watson!

James. Good-day to you, mum!

Mrs. Burrows [*closing and then reopening the door*]. I'll give you four and ninepence for a bag. [*James shakes his head.*] Five shillings, then.

James. Twelve shillings is my—no—I said threepence off. I'll tell you what I'll do, Mrs. Burrows; I'll call it eleven and sixpence. [*Mrs. Burrows, in answer, bangs the door.*] She'll come back. She's bound to have 'em.

[*Ever since Mrs. Burrows mentioned the two pounds of potatoes "of some new-fangled sort" Henry had listened with the greatest attention, and when she gave the name of "Elderberry," he had gone to the nearest bin, unfolded a newspaper that lay on it, and studied it with care.*]

Henry [*looking up excitedly*]. Dad!

James. What?

Henry. When Widow Burrows said "Elder-something," it came to me all of a sudden what she meant. And when she said Fennell's Elderberry, I was certain. I read about it this morning, here.

James. Who's been wasting their money buying papers? Have you?

Henry. It's to-day's *Bly Chronicle* that Bill Saunders lent me when I was out this morning. It's here, in black and white, all about the Potato Boom.

James. I'm sick of hearing all that cat-blash about

folks getting a pound apiece for potatoes. Now, is it likely? Who'd be fool enough to give it?

Henry [*reading*]. "The excitement in the potato trade continues. At Bly Market there was only one topic of conversation. The promise of the new varieties—Sutton's Discovery, Johnson's Diamond, Northern Star——"

James [*banging the table*]. The lies they tell makes my hair stand straight up.

Henry. It's not all lies, dad. Just listen! "Northern Star has proved a gold-mine to its lucky owners." [*James is about to protest against this waste of time, but these words cause him to relapse into his chair and listen carefully.*] "And every one is alert to secure the next favourite and make a rapid fortune. Mr. Findlay, who brought out the Up-to-Date, Evergood, Royal Kidney, and Northern Star, is reported to have a greater than all these up his sleeve. He sent several lots out, last spring, for trial, to various friends, who are most enthusiastic as to its possibilities. As the quantity is so limited the demand is enormous, and from a sovereign a pound they have risen, in a week, to the unheard-of price of forty pounds a pound. The new-comer promises to live up to its name of Eldorado."

James. We could have done with some of them, Henry. Forty sovereigns for a pound!

Henry. Don't you see, dad—that's the very name. That's what Widow Burrows was trying to say: Fennell's Elder something—Findlay's Eldorado. She's got some!

James [*starting up*]. Do you think so, boy?

Henry. I'm sure of it. The paper says, "Several small lots were sent out for trial," and Japhet Burrows's master, Lord Kyme, as is President of some big Society, would be the first to get them.

James. Well, that's a skelcher. Do you think it's true, Henry?

Henry [*still looking at the paper*]. Here's something else. "As we go to press, we learn that a stone of Eldorados has been sold by a local firm of potato merchants—Messrs. F. Mullen & Son—to Mr. Titus Ambrose of Holt-in-the Marsh at the incredible price of one hundred sovereigns per pound. The cheque for £1,400 is now on view in the window of our fortunate townsmen, and is the centre of the utmost excitement."

James. A hundred sovereigns a pound for potatoes! I shall never believe it.

Henry. The cheque is stuck up in Mullen's office window in Bly market-place. You can't get away from that.

James. Fourteen hundred pounds for a stone of potatoes! [*Suddenly*] Henry! What's Widow Burrows going to do with her two pound?

Henry [*promptly*]. Sell 'em for two hundred pounds, or else do the same as Moses Bellamy did last year with a pound of Northern Stars. He put them in his greenhouse, at Fletton, took the sprouts off into pots, and kept on at that, planting the cuttings out in his garden, till he got two hundredweights from his pound.

James. If I had any, I should *sell*, Henry.

Henry. They'll go dearer yet.

James. We've got to have them Eldorados. That woman couldn't use two hundred pounds: it 'ud be the ruin of her.

Henry. You wouldn't give that price?

James. What do you take me for? She knows nothing about that [*nodding at the paper*] yet.

Henry. She soon will.

James. Then we must move at once. Slip round and say as I've considered to let her have them Early Roses after all. Tell her to come in straightaway and look at 'em—pick her own bag—and then mention her Eldorados, casual-like, and get her to bring them in here to show me.

Henry. She'd smell a rat.

James. Not if you're crafty, Henry. You must be wily with her. Say we reckon we've got some of the same sort and should like to compare 'em. Be quick now, and don't you come back without her. [*Henry hurries out.*] A hundred sovereigns! Two hundred sovereigns! Fourteen hundred sovereigns! It's enough to craze anybody. It's a corker!

[*Betsy comes out of the scullery with a plate of bones.*]

Betsy. Where's them potatoes I asked you for an hour ago?

James [*who is studying the "Chronicle"*]. You don't mean to say as you've never fetched none?

Betsy [*crossing to front door*]. Didn't you promise to see about it?

James. I've plenty to think about, earning your living for you. Why didn't you go and fetch 'em yourself, when you saw it had slipped my memory?

Betsy [*standing on the platform outside the front door, whistling and throwing the bones down into the yard*]. There you are, Jack! [*She comes back into the room without closing the door.*] I'm not going paddling through that mucky yard for nobody.

James. You do what you're told.

Betsy. Why can't I have some of them Early Roses from upstairs? Goodness knows, there's plenty!

James [*looking up from his paper*]. I'll knock your head off if you touch them. They're valuable.

Betsy. I'm tired of this. Nothing but grumbling from morning till night, while I do a servant's work without any pay. I should be better off if I was out at service.

James. You ungrateful mawkin! After all I've done for you! If I hear anything of that again, out you go, neck and crop.

Betsy. That'll suit me down to the ground. I'll go to Doctor Walker's at Bly then. I see in the *Chronicle* that he wants a girl.

James. Think I should have a darter of mine in service! Just you slip off and get them potatoes.

[*He goes to the door and looks cautiously out.*]

Betsy. I'm not going through all that dirt again for nobody. Just look at my shoes!

[*She holds her foot out, but James takes no notice, so she stamps into the scullery, slamming the door.*]

James. Drat that Henry! Where's he got to? I ought to have gone myself. There they come! She's bringing them!

[*Retreating from the door, he sits down in his arm-chair, and is poking the fire when Henry and Mrs. Burrows come up the steps. Mrs. Burrows has a paper bag in her hand.*]

Mrs. Burrows. You've changed your mind, then?

James [*turning round*]. I've considered, Mrs. Burrows, what you said about being neighbourly—and a widow—and I've decided after all, there's something in it.

Mrs. Burrows [*suspiciously*]. I'm to have a bag at my price, am I?

James. What was your offer?

Mrs. Burrows [*promptly*]. Five shillings.

James [*staring at the bag in Mrs. Burrows's hand*]. It's fair murder. I wouldn't do it if you wasn't a widow.

Mrs. Burrows. I'll pay for 'em before you change your mind again. Where's my purse?

[*She puts the bag of potatoes down on the table, and feels for her purse.*]

James. What have you got there?

Mrs. Burrows [*producing a purse from her pocket*]. Them's the fancy potatoes as brother-in-law Japhet sent me. Your Henry says he thinks you've got some of the same sort, and would like to compare them.

James [*going to the table*]. There isn't two pounds there, surely?

Mrs. Burrows. They come in separate bags. I didn't bother to bring both. [*She empties the potatoes out on to the table. One rolls over the edge, but Henry catches it, with a horrified face.*] Nice colour, aren't they ?

James [*picking up the largest of the five tubers with religious care*]. Nothing to shout about.

Mrs. Burrows. Look at their deep eyes !

James. All the worse for cooking. They waste so much.

Mrs. Burrows. But the shape of them !

James. Wouldn't be many to a root, I lay !

Mrs. Burrows. Don't you like 'em, then ?

James. No, I don't. No good at all ! [*He turns away, then comes back, fascinated.*] No good at all !

Mrs. Burrows. Brother-in-law Japhet thought they was worth my trying, anyway, and he ought to know his trade.

James. Gardening isn't farming, though. What's all right for the gentry's table wouldn't answer for the likes of us. These wouldn't do for field growing.

Mrs. Burrows [*beginning to put the potatoes back in the bag*]. Deary me !

James [*poking the fire*]. If you take my advice, you'll chuck 'em to the pigs.

Mrs. Burrows. That would be a waste, Mr. Watson.

James. Betsy was bothering me just now for some potatoes for dinner. She might as well cook them, and I'll tell you how they eat.

Mrs. Burrows. I shouldn't like them to be cooked.

James. It's all they're fit for, I assure you.

Mrs. Burrows. Brother-in-law Japhet wouldn't like it.

James [*feeling in his pocket*]. It'll save Betsy getting messed up. I'll give you tuppence for 'em—that's over two shillings a stone.

Henry [*chiming in*]. Nearly twenty pounds a ton !

James [*holding out coppers*]. There's threepence

ha'penny. There you are! I shouldn't do it, only the gel's been worrying me so.

[*He takes the bag from Mrs. Burrows and puts the coppers on the table.*]

Mrs. Burrows. I couldn't, really.

James. Why not?

Mrs. Burrows. Brother-in-law Japhet wanted me to grow 'em, and he wouldn't like it.

James. I'll give you sixpence, then.

Mrs. Burrows. Brother-in-law Ja——

James [*bursting out irritably*]. Confound brother-in-law Japhet! Keep your potatoes!

Mrs. Burrows [*taking the bag from him*]. I think he'd rather I planted 'em. [*She sees the largest tuber in James's hand and reaches out for it.*] Thank you!

James [*waving her off*]. Wait a minute! [*He looks carefully at the Eldorado.*] I don't know, after all, as they mightn't answer in our garden, Henry. I almost think, Mrs. Burrows, as I will set 'em and see how they turn out.

Mrs. Burrows. You said they wasn't any use at all, just now.

James. I think so still, only I like to try new things. Look here! I'll give you a peck of Early Roses in exchange.

[*Mrs. Burrows's suspicions have now come to a head. She looks at James, then at Henry, then at the bag in her hand, and with tightened lips reaches for the largest Eldorado that James still clasps.*]

James. Is that a bargain?

Mrs. Burrows. I'll plant 'em myself. Brother-in-law Japhet sent them on purpose.

James [*edging away from her*]. You've got a pound left, ain't you? We can both try 'em. I'll give you two pecks of Early Roses.

Mrs. Burrows [*still holding her hand out*]. No, I'll keep them. Give us hold of that.

James. Don't be in such a hurry. I'll do you a level

swop—the bag of Early Roses as you want so bad, for this pound.

Mrs. Burrows. Brother-in-law Japhet wouldn't have sent them if they hadn't been something extra special.

James. What *do* you want then, woman ?

Mrs. Burrows. My potato.

[*She seizes the one in old Watson's hand, drops it into the bag, and turns to go. James hurries between her and the door.*]

James. Now look here, Mrs. Burrows ; I'll buy 'em if you'll be ruly and set a price. Come now, what is it ?

Mrs. Burrows [*looking at him for a moment in silence*]. What about them seven young pigs as I tried to buy from you, and you wouldn't part with ?

James. I told you I couldn't sell them. Their father won a prize at Barkston Show.

Mrs. Burrows. I bid you nineteen shillings apiece.

James. But they're not for sale.

Mrs. Burrows. If you offered to give me that sack of Early Roses for this pound [*she holds the bag up, and James puts his hand out eagerly*], and throw in that litter of black pigs, I might consider it.

James. What ! My prize pigs ! You're crazed ! Talk sense, woman. If you'd asked for one now——

Mrs. Burrows. You'd have closed with me, shouldn't you ? You're strange and keen for this pound of potatoes.

[*Henry, who has been making signs to his father behind Mrs. Burrows's back, sits down suddenly, the picture of despair.*]

James. Keen ? Me ? Not a bit ! Keep 'em ! Keep 'em !

Mrs. Burrows. I'm going to.

James [*catching her arm*]. Be reasonable, woman. I'll try and buy them.

Mrs. Burrows. I am reasonable. As you said a bit since : business is business, and if you want my potatoes, you've got to pay my price for them.

James. My prize pigs! I couldn't.

Mrs. Burrows. Then good-day to you!

[*As she puts her hand on the latch, Henry signals wildly to his father.*]

James. All right! They're yours.

Mrs. Burrows. Oh no! Not now. You should have took my offer when I made it.

James. Look here! Say straight out what you do want.

Mrs. Burrows [*coming back to the table*]. I want that sack of Early Roses, the litter of black pigs, [*she points to the ham hanging from the beam*] that ham, [*she considers for a moment*] . . . and thirty shillings.

James. You never said nothing about a ham and thirty shillings.

Mrs. Burrows. Is it a deal? I shan't wait.

James [*wildly*]. Yes, drat you!

Mrs. Burrows [*putting the Eldorados on the table*]. There you are, then. Where's the money?

James [*putting the money on the table*]. You—you—
[*He chokes with spleen.*]

Mrs. Burrows [*calmly*]. Hook my ham down, Henry, and don't bruise it.

James. I'll do that. Fetch a bag of Early Roses down, and then tell young Fox to drive them pigs across.

[*Henry hurries upstairs, whilst James gets on a chair and hooks down the ham.*]

Mrs. Burrows [*taking the ham*]. This is a nice mellow ham, this is. Better'n the scrawdy bacon as I've been having for breakfast lately.

James. You've done me this time, missis.

Mrs. Burrows. You pleased yourself. Do you want to run back? [*James shakes his head.*] I've been a fool; that's what I've been! I see it now. You'd have given more.

James. No, you hard nailer! You've shaved me clean. My prize pigs!

Scrawdy, Fat, with only a thin streak of lean.

[*The left-hand trap-doors are lifted, and as Henry calls "Below, there," James walks across to the chain, which begins to move. As a sack of potatoes swings into sight, James steadies the chain, and when the bag reaches the floor, unfastens the slip hook from its neck and lays the bag over on its side. Henry closes the trap-doors.*]

James. What about the other pound?

Mrs. Burrows. I wouldn't sell them for no money.

James. Oh yes, you would!

Mrs. Burrows. I tell you I wouldn't . . . I wouldn't take twenty pounds for 'em.

James. Twenty pounds!

Mrs. Burrows. No, I wouldn't. Brother-in-law Japhet——

James. Take ten.

Mrs. Burrows. Now, is it likely? You've given me more for *that* pound. [*Henry comes down the steps, goes over to the zinc plate, takes hold of the bag of Early Roses, and with an adroit jerk throws them over his shoulder, and walks out of the door with them.*] You must think me a fool.

James. All right, then! Twenty pound!

Mrs. Burrows. Certainly not! I said I wouldn't take twenty pounds; and I won't. They're not for sale.

James. Oh, we know all about that. Everything has its price.

Mrs. Burrows [*picking the ham off the table and going to the door*]. That's just where you're wrong. I shall keep my pound and see what happens.

James [*contemptuously*]. What do *you* know about new sorts of potatoes?

Mrs. Burrows [*turning in the doorway*]. Nothing at all. But I know a good deal about *you,* Jim Watson. [*Looking to the left, towards the road.*] There goes my prize pigs.

James. Thirty pounds, then!

Mrs. Burrows [*shaking her head scornfully*]. I should have took sixpence for them potatoes, only your eyes were so greedy. I may be only a woman, but I can tell when you're anxious. It's nice to get the best of you, just for once.

[*Carrying the ham in front of her, she descends the steps and disappears. James stares after her with a discomfited air ; then recollects himself, goes to the table, picks up the bag, and reads aloud,* FINDLAY'S ELDORADO. *He looks round thoughtfully, and his eye falls on the egg-basket standing on the chair. He takes out the tubers one by one, placing them in the basket.*]

James. I'll fetch my cash-box down and lock 'em in that. I could keep 'em in yon cupboard by the stove : it 'ud be warm there.

[*He goes up the steps. As the trap-door closes behind him the scullery door opens, and Betsy is seen in the doorway, standing in a defiant attitude, with her hands on her hips. But there is no one to defy, so with a toss of her head she makes for the front door, to be brought to a standstill by the sight of the basket of potatoes.*]

Betsy [*with great scorn*]. Five potatoes for three people!

[*Holding up her apron, she tilts the potatoes in and replaces the basket. Its lid falls down. Betsy returns to her stronghold and closes the door. The trap-door opens, and James comes down with a large cash-box under his arm. As he reaches the floor Henry hurries in from the yard.*]

Henry [*excitedly*]. We've got 'em !

James [*pulling out a bunch of keys and trying to find one that will fit the cash-box*]. At a price.

Henry. It was all your own fault. You should have closed with her quicker. [*He sees the empty paper bag that James has replaced on the table.*] Where are they ?

James. In that basket ; but I'm going to lock 'em up in this—if I can find the key. Here ! just see if you've one that'll fit it.

Henry [*producing a bunch*]. It must go under our bed, dad. Suppose anybody stole them.

James. Don't, boy. You make me all of a sweat. I wish I had an iron safe.

Henry. You couldn't get the other pound, then ?

James. No, confound all widows ! Hallo !

[*Mrs. Burrows is seen hurrying up the steps. She enters the room, still carrying the ham, which she plants on the table.*]

James [*uneasily*]. Back again, Mrs. Burrows ?

Mrs. Burrows. You thief. Robbing a poor widow ! But I'll show you up ; I'll expose you if you don't give me my Eldorados back. Where are they ?

[*Henry, at her first word, edged away from the table, and now stands with his back to the egg-basket, hiding it from view.*]

James. What's this all about ?

Mrs. Burrows. What's it all about ? You know very well what it's all about. This telegram was waiting at the door when I got home—from brother-in-law Japhet. [*She holds up a telegram and reads.*] JUST HEARD ELDORADOS SENT YOU WORTH TWO HUNDRED POUNDS. LOCK THEM UP. COMING ONE THIRTY-FIVE. — JAPHET. You scanny rascal — you knew it.

James. I don't know what you mean.

Mrs. Burrows. You just give 'em back to me. Where are they ?

James. Bought *and* paid for.

Mrs. Burrows [*pushing the ham across the table towards him*]. You can have your pigs and all the rest of your kelter back again. Where's my Eldorados ?

James. Business is business, Mrs. Burrows. You

Kelter, Rubbish.

thought you'd diddled me—well, you didn't, that's all! Anyway, you've got one pound left.

Mrs. Burrows. I want them both. What will brother-in-law Japhet say?

James. I've nothing to do with your brother-in-law Japhet, nor him with me, neither.

Mrs. Burrows. Oh, haven't you? Wait till he comes: he'll wring your neck—you little ferret!

James. I shall have him locked up if he comes brawling here.

Mrs. Burrows [*a little daunted, remembering Japhet's ungovernable temper*]. We don't want no policemen interfering.

James. Then be ruly! A bargain's a bargain, and it's no use chuntering. [*He pushes the ham back.*]

Mrs. Burrows. You lied to me so—saying you wanted 'em for your dinner!

James [*pulling his purse out*]. Here! One—two—three sovereigns. All I've got. I'll throw that in if you hold your noise and call it quits. If you don't, Henry fetches Tom Arch. You know how hot-tempered your brother-in-law is, and if you go and sing a song to him about this, there's bound to be a row, and he'll get locked up as sure as eggs is eggs. [*He holds out the money to her.*] Come on, now! It's no use roaring.

Mrs. Burrows [*wavering*]. Make it ten pounds.

James [*sharply*]. Not a copper more. Take it or leave it.

Mrs. Burrows [*taking the cash and picking up her ham*]. But I don't know what I shall tell brother-in-law Japhet!

James. You can come away from that chair now, Henry.

Mrs. Burrows. Oh, that's where they was! [*She steps across and raises the basket lid.*] Why, it's empty!

Chuntering, Grumbling.

Henry and James [*rushing forward and shouting together*]. What !

James. She's took 'em. Hold her, Henry.

Mrs. Burrows. Don't be a fool. How could I, with you gaping at me all the time ?

James. I put 'em in there out of the bag. I'll swear I did. [*The two men search frantically, whilst Mrs. Burrows watches with interest ; but there are so few places in which to look that in a very short time they are staring blankly at each other. The scullery door opens and Betsy appears with a saucepan in her hand, evidently disturbed by the noise.*] Betsy ! I put some potatoes in that basket. Have you seen them ?

Betsy. In that basket ?

James. Yes. Wake up ! Have you moved them ?

Betsy. Of course I moved them.

James [*with an air of enormous relief*]. Where have you put them ? Where are they ?

Betsy. Where are they ? [*Holding the saucepan under James's nose.*] They're here, of course. Where do you think ?

Together {
James. Ruined ! My Eldorados ! My prize pigs !
Henry. Oh, my hat, Betsy. What *have* you done ?
Mrs. Burrows. Well, I never. If she hasn't gone and peeled them !

Betsy [*to Mrs. Burrows*]. Of course I peeled them ! [*To her father.*] Didn't you put them there for me ?

[*James and Henry are speechless.*]

Mrs. Burrows. Serve you right ! Serve you right ! You said you wanted them for your dinner, and you've got them. [*She opens the door.*] Ten pounds a mouthful ! I HOPE YOU'LL ENJOY YOUR DINNER !

[*She closes the door.*]

CURTAIN

CAMPBELL OF KILMOHR

By J. A. Ferguson

This is the definitive edition of *Campbell of Kilmohr*, with the author's final revisions of the text, made especially for this volume, and his Acting Notes (see page 219). The correct spelling of the title is that given here.
This play is published separately by Thomas Nelson and Sons, Ltd., at 1s. net.

EDITOR'S PREFACE

The scene of the play is the Highlands of Scotland, in the winter of the year 1746. George II. was King of England, but in the Highlands many people still believed that the rightful king was Charles Edward Stuart, grandson of James II., who is known in history as the Young Pretender. He had landed in Scotland with seven followers in July 1745, gathered his Highland supporters, who were charmed by his gallant and attractive personality, entered Edinburgh, and marched south to within a hundred and twenty miles of London before he was compelled to retreat. He won a victory at Falkirk, but in April 1746 his army was overwhelmed at Culloden by the Duke of Cumberland, who had trained his men to meet the terrible charge of the Highlanders. With a reward of £30,000 offered for his capture, and armies searching the country for him, Charles Edward became a fugitive in the Highlands; but through all his adventures and hardships and hairbreadth escapes, the bravery of Flora Macdonald and the passionate loyalty of his friends kept him safe, and he escaped to France at the end of the year 1746. How loyal his followers were, and how they hated Scotsmen who were on the side of King George, we learn in this play from Mary and Dugald Stewart. They are as determined to save their Prince and his friends, who are in hiding not far away, as Campbell of Kilmohr is anxious to get the £30,000 reward.

Produced by the Scottish Repertory Theatre Company at the Royalty Theatre, Glasgow, on Monday, March 23, 1914, with the following cast:

MARY STEWART	Miss Agnes Lowson.
MORAG CAMERON	Miss Rita Thom.
DUGALD STEWART . . .	Mr. Nicholas Hannen.
CAPTAIN SANDEMAN . . .	Mr. N. N. Wimbush.
ARCHIBALD CAMPBELL . .	Mr. W. S. Hartford.
JAMES MACKENZIE . . .	Mr. C. Stewart Robertson.

SCENE.—Interior of a lonely cottage on the road from Struan to Rannoch in North Perthshire.

TIME.—After the Rising of '45.

The Play produced by Mr. Lewis Casson.

CAMPBELL OF KILMOHR

Morag is restlessly moving backwards and forwards. The old woman is seated on a low stool beside the peat fire in the centre of the floor.

The room is scantily furnished and the women are poorly clad. Morag is barefooted. At the back is the door that leads to the outside. On the left of the door is a small window. On the right side of the room there is a door that opens into a barn. Morag stands for a moment at the window, looking out.

Morag. It is the wild night outside.

Mary Stewart. Is the snow still coming down?

Morag. It is that then—dancing and swirling with the wind too, and never stopping at all. Aye, and so black I cannot see the other side of the road.

Mary Stewart. That is good.

[*Morag moves across the floor and stops irresolutely. She is restless, expectant.*]

Morag. Will I be putting the light in the window?

Mary Stewart. Why should you be doing that! You have not heard his call [*turns eagerly*], have you?

Morag [*with sign of head*]. No, but the light in the window would show him all is well.

Mary Stewart. It would not then! The light was to be put there *after* we had heard the signal.

Morag. But on a night like this he may have been calling for long and we never hear him.

Mary Stewart. Do not be so anxious, Morag. Keep to what he says. Put more peat on the fire now and sit down.

Morag [*with increasing excitement*]. I canna, I canna! There is that in me that tells me something is going to befall us this night. Oh, that wind, hear to it, sobbing round the house as if it brought some poor lost soul up to the door, and we refusing it shelter.

Mary Stewart. Do not be fretting yourself like that. Do as I bid you. Put more peats to the fire.

Morag [*at the wicker peat-basket*]. Never since I . . . What was that? [*Both listen for a moment.*]

Mary Stewart. It was just the wind; it is rising more. A sore night for them that are out in the heather.

[*Morag puts peat on the fire without speaking.*]

Mary Stewart. Did you notice were there many people going by to-day?

Morag. No. After daybreak the redcoats came by from Struan; and there was no more till nine, when an old man like the Catechist from Killichonan passed. At four o'clock, just when the dark was falling, a horseman with a lad holding to the stirrup, and running fast, went by towards Rannoch.

Mary Stewart. But no more redcoats?

Morag [*shaking her head*]. The road has been as quiet as the hills, and they as quiet as the grave. Do you think he will come?

Mary Stewart. Is it you think I have the gift, girl, that you ask me that? All I know is that it is five days since he was here for meat and drink for himself and for the others—five days and five nights, mind you; and little enough he took away; and those in hiding no' used to sore lying I'll be thinking. He must try to get through to-night. But that quietness, with no one to be seen from daylight till dark, I do not like it, Morag. They must know something. They must be watching.

[*A sound is heard by both women. They stand listening.*]

Mary Stewart. Haste you with the light, Morag.

Morag. But it came from the back of the house—from the hillside.

Mary Stewart. Do as I tell you. The other side may be watched.

[*A candle is lit and placed in the window. Girl goes hurrying to the door.*]

Mary Stewart. Stop, stop! Would you be opening the door with a light like that shining from the house? A man would be seen against it in the doorway for a mile. And who knows what eyes may be watching? Put out the light now and cover the fire.

[*Room is reduced to semi-darkness, and the door unbarred. Some one enters.*]

Morag. You are cold, Dugald!

[*Stewart, very exhausted, signs assent.*]

Morag. And wet, oh, wet through and through!

Stewart. Erricht Brig was guarded, well guarded. I had to win across the water.

[*The old woman has now relit candle and taken away plaid from fire.*]

Mary Stewart. Erricht Brig—then——

Stewart [*nods*]. Yes—in a corrie, on the far side of Dearig, half-way up.

Mary Stewart. Himself is there then?

Stewart. Aye, and Keppoch as well, and another and a greater is with them.

Mary Stewart. Wheest! [*Glances at Morag.*]

Stewart. Mother, is it that you can . . .

Mary Stewart. Yes, yes, Morag will bring out the food for ye to carry back. It is under the hay in the barn, well hid. Morag will bring it. Go, Morag, and bring it.

[*Morag enters other room or barn which opens on right.*]

Stewart. Mother, I wonder at ye; Morag would never tell—never.

Mary Stewart. Morag is only a lass yet. She has

never been tried. And who knows what she might be made to tell.

Stewart. Well, well, it is no matter, for I was telling you where I left them, but not where I am to *find* them.

Mary Stewart. They are not where you said now?

Stewart. No; they left the corrie last night, and I am to find them [*whispers*] in a quiet part on Rannoch Moor.

Mary Stewart. It is well for a young lass not to be knowing. Do not tell her.

Stewart. Well, well, I will not tell her. Then she cannot tell where they are even if she wanted to.

[*He sits down at table; the old woman ministers to his wants.*]

Stewart. A fire is a merry thing on a night like this; and a roof over the head is a great comfort.

Mary Stewart. Ye'll no' can stop the night?

Stewart. No. I must be many a mile from here before the day breaks on Ben Dearig.

[*Morag re-enters.*]

Morag. It was hard to get through, Dugald?

Stewart. You may say that. I came down Erricht for three miles, and then when I reached low country I had to take to walking in the burns because of the snow that shows a man's steps and tells who he is to them that can read; and there's plenty can do that abroad, God knows.

Morag. But none spied ye?

Stewart. Who can tell? Before dark came, from far up on the slopes of Dearig I saw soldiers down below; and away towards Rannoch Moor they were scattered all over the country like black flies on a white sheet. A wild-cat or anything that couldna fly could never have got through. And men at every brig and ford and pass! I had to strike away up across the slopes again; and even so as I turned round the bend beyond Kilrain I ran straight into a sentry sheltering behind a great rock. But after that it was easy going.

Morag. How could that be ?

Stewart. Well, you see, I took the boots off him, and then I had no need to mind who might see my steps in the snow.

Morag. You took the boots off him !

Stewart [*laughing*]. I did that same. Does that puzzle your bonny head ? How does a lad take the boots off a redcoat ? Find out the answer, my lass, while I will be finishing my meat.

Morag. Maybe he was asleep ?

Stewart. Asleep ! Asleep ! Well, well, he sleeps sound enough now, with the ten toes of him pointed to the sky.

[*The old woman has taken up dirk from table. She puts it down again. Morag sees the action, and pushes dirk away so that it rolls off the table and drops to the floor. She hides her face in her hands.*]

Mary Stewart. Morag, bring in the kebbuck o' cheese. Now that all is well and safe it is we that will look after his comfort to-night. [*Morag goes into barn.*] I mind well her mother saying to me—it was one day in the black winter that she died, when the frost took the land in its grip and the birds fell stiff from the trees, and the deer came down and put their noses to the door—I mind well her saying just before she died—— [*Loud knocking at the door*].

A Voice. In the King's name ! [*Both rise, startled.*]

Mary Stewart [*recovering first*]. The hay in the barn—quick, my son. [*Knocking continues.*]

A Voice. Open in the King's name !

[*Stewart snatches up such articles as would reveal his presence and hurries into barn. He overlooks dirk on floor. The old woman goes towards door, slowly, to gain time.*]

Mary Stewart. Who is there ? What do you want ?

A Voice. Open, open.

[*Mary Stewart opens door, and Campbell of Kilmohr follows Captain Sandeman into the house. Behind Kilmohr comes a man carrying a leather wallet, James Mackenzie, his clerk. The rear is brought up by soldiers carrying arms.*]

Sandeman. Ha, the bird has flown.

Campbell [*who has struck dirk with his foot and picked it up*]. But the nest is warm ; look at this.

Sandeman. It seems as if we had disturbed him at supper. Search the house, men.

Mary Stewart. I'm just a lonely old woman. You have been misguided. I was getting through my supper.

Campbell [*holding up dirk*]. And this was your toothpick, eh ? Na ! na ! We ken whaur we are, and wha we want, and, by Cruachan, I think we've got him.

[*Sounds are heard from barn, and soldiers return with Morag. She has stayed in hiding from fear, and she still holds the cheese in her hands.*

Sandeman. What have we here !

Campbell. A lass !

Mary Stewart. It's just my dead brother's daughter. She was getting me the cheese, as you can see.

Campbell. On men, again: the other turtle-doo will no' be far away. [*Bantering, to the old woman.*] Tut, tut, Mistress Stewart, and do ye have her wait upon ye while your leddyship dines alane! A grand way to treat your dead brother's daughter; fie, fie, upon ye!

[*Soldiers reappear with Stewart, whose arms are pinioned.*]

Campbell. Did I no' tell ye ! And this, Mrs. Stewart, will be your dead sister's son, I'm thinking ; or aiblins your leddyship's butler ! Weel, woman,

Aiblins, Perhaps.

I'll tell ye this: Pharaoh spared ae butler, but Erchie Campbell will no spare anither. Na! na! Pharaoh's case is no' to be taken as forming ony preceedent. And so if he doesna answer certain questions we have to speir at him, before morning he'll hang as high as Haman.

[*Stewart is placed before the table at which Campbell has seated himself. Two soldiers guard Stewart. Another is behind Campbell's chair and another is by the door. The clerk, Mackenzie, is seated at up corner of table. Sandeman stands by the fire.*

Campbell [*to Stewart*]. Weel, sir, it is within the cognizance of the law that you have knowledge and information of the place of harbour and concealment used by certain persons who are in a state of proscription. Furthermore, it is known that four days ago certain other proscribed persons did join with these, and that they are banded together in an endeavour to secure the escape from these dominions of His Majesty, King George, of certain persons who by their crimes and treasons lie open to the capital charge. What say ye? [*Stewart makes no reply.*]

Campbell. Ye admit this then?

[*Stewart as before.*]

Campbell. Come, come, my lad. Ye stand in great jeopardy. Great affairs of state lie behind this which are beyond your simple understanding. Speak up, and it will be the better for ye.

[*Stewart silent as before.*]

Campbell. Look you. I'll be frank with you. No harm will befall you this night (and I wish all in this house to note my words)—no harm will befall you this night if you supply the information required.

[*Stewart as before.*]

Campbell [*with sudden passion*]. Sandeman, put

Speir, Ask.

your sword to the carcass o' this muckle ass and see will it louse his tongue. [*Sandeman does not move.*]

Stewart. It may be as well then, Mr. Campbell, that I should say a word to save your breath. It is this: Till you talk Rannoch Loch to the top of Schiehallion ye'll no' talk me into a yea or nay.

Campbell [*quietly*]. Say ye so? Noo, I wadna be so very sure if I were you. I've had a lairge experience o' life, and speaking out of it I would say that only fools and the dead never change their minds.

Stewart [*quietly too*]. Then you'll be adding to your experience to-night, Mr. Campbell, and you'll have something to put on to the other side of it.

Campbell [*tapping his snuff-box*]. Very possibly, young sir, but what I would present for your consideration is this: While ye may be prepared to keep your mouth shut under the condition of a fool, are ye equally prepared to do so in the condition of a dead man?

[*Campbell waits expectantly. Stewart silent as before.*]

Campbell. Tut, tut, now if it's afraid ye are, my lad, with my hand on my heart and on my word as a gentleman . . .

Stewart. Afraid!

[*He spits in contempt towards Campbell.*]

Campbell [*enraged*]. Ye damned stubborn Hieland stot . . . [*To Sandeman*] Have him taken out. We'll get it another way.

[*Campbell rises. Stewart is moved into barn by soldiers, who remain with him.*]

Campbell [*walking*]. Some puling eediots, Sandeman, would applaud this contumacy and call it constancy. Constancy! Now, I've had a lairge experience o' life, and I never saw yet a sensible man insensible to the touch of yellow metal. If there may

Muckle, Great. *Stot*, Bullock.

be such a man, it is demonstrable that he is no sensible man. Fideelity! quotha, it's sheer obstinacy. They just see that ye want something oot o' them, and they're so damned selfish and thrawn they winna pairt. And with the natural inabeelity o' their brains to hold mair than one idea at a time, they canna see that in return you could put something into their palms far more profitable. [*Sits again at table.*] Aweel, bring Mistress Stewart up.

[*Old woman is placed before him where son had been.*]

Campbell [*more ingratiatingly*]. Weel noo, Mistress Stewart, good woman, this is a sair predeecament for ye to be in. I would jist counsel ye to be candid. Doubtless yer mind is a' in a swirl. Ye kenna what way to turn. Maybe ye are like the Psalmist and say: "I lookit this way and that, and there was no man to peety me, or to have compassion upon my fatherless children." But, see now, ye would be wrong; and, if ye tell me a' ye ken, I'll stand freends wi' ye. Put your trust in Erchie Campbell.

Mary Stewart. I trust no Campbell.

Campbell. Weel, weel, noo, I'm no' jist that set up wi' them myself. There's but ae Campbell that I care muckle aboot, after a'. But, good wife, it's no' the Campbells we're trying the noo; so, as time presses, we'll jist *birze yont,* as they say themselves. Noo then, speak up. [*Mary Stewart is silent.*]

Campbell [*beginning grimly and, passing through astonishment, expostulation, and a feigned contempt for mother and pity for son, to a pretence of sadness which, except at the end, makes his words come haltingly*]. Ah! ye also. I suppose ye understand, woman, how it will go wi' your son? [*To his clerk.*] Here's a fine mother for ye, James! Would you believe it? She kens what would save her son—the very babe she nursed at her breast: but will she save him? Na!

Kenna, Know not. *Birze yont*, Press forward.

na! Sir, he may look after himself! A mother, a mother! Ha! ha!

[*Campbell laughs. Mackenzie titters foolishly. Campbell pauses to watch effect of his words.*]

Aye, you would think, James, that she would remember the time when he was but little and afraid of all the terrors that walk in darkness, and how he looked up to her as to a tower of safety, and would run to her with outstretched hands, hiding his face from his fear, in her gown. The darkness! It is the dark night and a long journey before him now.

[*He pauses again.*]

You would think, James, that she would mind how she happit him from the cold of winter and sheltered him from the summer heats, and, when he began to find his footing, how she had an eye on a' the beasts of the field, and on the water and the fire that were become her enemies. And to what purpose ali this care?—tell me that, my man, to what good, if she is to leave him at the last to dangle from a tree at the end of a hempen rope—to see his flesh to be meat for the fowls of the air—her son, her little son!

Mary Stewart [*softly*]. My son—my little son! . . . Oh, [*more loudly*] but my son he has done no crime.

Campbell. Has he no'? Weel, mistress, as ye'll no' take my word for it, maybe ye'll list to Mr. Mackenzie here. What say ye, James?

Mackenzie. He is guilty of aiding and abetting in the concealment of proscribed persons; likewise with being found in the possession of arms, contrary to statute, both very heinous crimes.

Campbell. Very well said, James! Forby, between ourselves, Mrs. Stewart, the young man in my opeenion is guilty of another crime [*snuffs*]—he is guilty of the heinous crime of not knowing on which side his bread is buttered. Come now. . . .

Happit, Covered. *Forby*, Besides.

Mary Stewart. Ye durst not lay a finger on the lad, ye durst not hang him.

Mackenzie. And why should the gentleman not hang him if it pleesure him?

[*Campbell taps snuff-box and takes pinch.*]

Mary Stewart [*with intensity*]. Campbell of Kilmohr, lay but one finger on Dugald Stewart and the weight of Ben Cruachan will be light to the weight that will be laid on your soul. I will lay the curse of the seven rings upon your life. I will call up the fires of Ephron, the blue and the green and the grey fires, for the destruction of your soul. I will curse you in your homestead and in the wife it shelters, and in the children that will never bear your name. Yea and ye shall be cursed.

Campbell [*startled, betrays agitation—the snuff is spilt from his trembling hand*]. Hoot toot, woman! ye're, ye're . . . [*Angrily.*] Ye auld beldame, to say such things to me! I'll have ye first whippit and syne droont for a witch. Damn thae stubborn and supersteetious cattle! [*To Sandeman.*] We should have come in here before him and listened in the barn, Sandeman!

Sandeman [*in quick staccato, always cool*]. Ah, listen behind the door you mean! Now I never thought of that!

Campbell. Did ye not! Humph! Well, no doubt there are a good many things in the universe that yet wait for your thought upon them. What would be your objections, now?

Sandeman. There are two objections, Kilmohr, that you would understand.

Campbell. Name them.

Sandeman. Well, in the first place, we have not wings like crows to fly . . . and the footsteps on the snow. . . . Second point: the woman would have told him we were there.

Syne droont, Then drowned.

Campbell. Not if I told her I had the power to clap her in Inverness jail.

Mary Stewart [*in contempt*]. Yes, even if ye had told me ye had power to clap me in hell, Mr. Campbell.

Campbell. Lift me that screeching Jezebel oot o' here; Sandeman, we'll mak' a quick finish o' this. [*Soldiers take her towards barn.*] No, not there, pitch the old girzie into the snow.

Mary Stewart [*as she is led outside*]. Ye'll never find him, Campbell, never, never!

Campbell [*enraged*]. Find him, aye, by God I'll find him, if I have to keek under every stone on the mountains from the Boar of Badenoch to the Sow of Athole. [*Old woman and soldiers go outside, leaving only Campbell, Mackenzie, Sandeman, and Morag in the room; Morag huddled up on stool.*] And now, Captain Sandeman, you an' me must have a word or two. I noted your objection to listening ahint doors and so on. Now, I make a' necessary allowances for youth and the grand and magneeficent ideas commonly held, for a little while, in that period. I had them myself. But, man, gin ye had trod the floor of the Parliament Hoose in Edinburry as long as I did, wi' a pair o' thin hands at the bottom o' toom pockets, ye'd ha'e shed your fine notions, as I did. Noo, fine pernickety noansense will no' do in this business——

Sandeman. Sir!

Campbell. Softly, softly, Captain Sandeman, and hear till what I have to say. I have noticed with regret several things in your remarks and bearing which are displeasing to me. I would say just one word in your ear; it is this: These things, Sandeman, are not conducive to advancement in His Majesty's service.

Sandeman [*after a brief pause in which the two eye*

Girzie, Noisy woman. *Toom*, Empty.

each other]. Kilmohr, I am a soldier, and if I speak out my mind you must pardon me if my words are blunt: I do not like this work, but I *loathe* your methods.

Campbell. Mislike the methods you may, but the work ye must do! Methods are my business. Let me tell you the true position. In ae word it is no more and no less than this. You and me are baith here to carry out the proveesions of the Act for the Pacification of the Highlands. That means the cleaning up of a very big mess, Sandeman, a very big mess. Now, what is your special office in this work? I'll tell ye, man; you and your men are just beesoms in the hands of the law-officers of the Crown. In this district, I order and ye soop. [*He indicates door of barn.*] Now soop, Captain Sandeman.

Sandeman. What are you after? I would give something to see into your mind.

Campbell. Ne'er fash aboot my mind: what has a soldier to do with ony mental operations? It's His Grace's orders that concern you. Oot wi' your man and set him up against the wa'.

Sandeman. Kilmohr, it is murder—murder, Kilmohr!

Campbell. Hoots awa', man, it's a thing o' nae special signeeficence.

Sandeman. I must ask you for a warrant.

Campbell. Quick, then: Mackenzie will bring it out to you.

[*Clerk begins writing as Sandeman goes and orders the soldiers to lead Stewart outside. Campbell sits very still and thoughtful. Clerk finishes writing and places warrant before Campbell for his signature.*

Mackenzie. At this place, sir.

Campbell [*again alert*]. Hoots, I was forgetting.

Mackenzie. It is a great power ye have in your hands, Kilmohr, to be able to send a man to death on the nod, as ye might say.

Campbell [*sitting back, pen in hand*]. Power! power say ye? Man, do ye no' see I've been beaten. Do ye no' see that? Archibald Campbell and a' his men and his money are less to them than the wind blowing in their faces.

Mackenzie. Well, it's a strange thing that.

Campbell [*throwing down the pen and rising*]. Aye, it's a strange thing that. It's a thing fit to sicken a man against the notion that there are probabilities on this earth. . . . Ye see, James, beforehand I would have said nothing could be easier.

Mackenzie. Than to get them to tell?

Campbell. Aye, just that. But you heard what he said: "You'll be adding to your experience this night, Mr. Campbell, and you'll have something to put to the other side of it," says he. [*Paces away, hands behind back.*] Aye, and I have added something to it, a thing I like but little. [*Turning to face Mackenzie with raised hand.*] Do you see what it is, James? A dream can be stronger than a strong man armed. Just a whispered word, a pointed finger even, would ha'e tell'd us a'. But no! no! And so I am powerless before the visions and dreams of an old woman and a half-grown lad.

Mackenzie [*who now stands waiting for the warrant*]. No' exactly powerless, Kilmohr, for if ye canna open his mouth ye can shut it; and there's some satisfaction in that.

Campbell [*sitting down to sign warrant*]. No' to me, man, no' to me. [*He hands the paper to Mackenzie, who goes out.*] For I've been beaten. Aye, the pair o' them have beat me, though it's only a matter o' seconds till one o' them be dead.

Morag [*her voice coming quickly, in a sharp whisper, like an echo of Campbell's last word as she sits up to stare at him*]. Dead!

Campbell [*startled*]. What is that?

Morag [*slowly*]. Is he dead?

Campbell [*aloud*]. Oh, it's you. I'd forgotten you were there.

Morag [*in same tone*]. Is he dead ?

Campbell [*grimly*]. Not yet. But if ye'll look through this window preesently ye'll see him gotten ready for death.

[*He picks up hat, gloves, cloak, and is about to go out.*]

Morag [*after a pause, very slowly and brokenly*]. I—will—tell—you.

Campbell [*astounded*]. What !

Morag I will tell you all you are seeking to know.

Campbell [*in a whisper, thunderstruck*]. God, and to think, to think I was on the very act . . . on the very act of . . . [*Recovering.*] Tell me—tell me at once.

Morag. You will promise that he will not be hanged ?

Campbell. He will not. I swear it.

Morag. You will give him back to me ?

Campbell. I will give him back—unhung.

Morag. Then [*Campbell comes near*], in a corrie half-way up the far side of Dearig—God save me !

Campbell [*in exultation*]. Dished after a'. I've clean dished them ! Loard, Loard ! [*With intense solemnity, clasping hands and looking upwards.*] Once more I can believe in the rationality of Thy world. [*Gathers up again his cloak, hat, etc.*] And to think . . . to think . . . I was on the very act of going away like a beaten dog !

Morag. He is safe from hanging now ?

Campbell [*chuckles and looks out at window before replying, and is at door when he speaks*]. Very near it, very near it. Listen !

[*He holds up his hand—a volley of musketry is heard. Kilmohr goes out, leaving door wide open. After a short interval of silence, the old woman enters and advances a few steps towards the girl, who has sunk on her knees at the volley.*]

Mary Stewart. Did you hear, Morag Cameron, did you hear?

[*The girl is sobbing, her face covered by her hands.*]

Mary Stewart. Och! be quiet now. I would be listening till the last sound of it passes into the great hills and over all the wide world. . . . It is fitting for you to be crying, a child that cannot understand, but water shall never wet eye of mine for Dugald Stewart. Last night I was but the mother of a lad that herded sheep on the Athole hills: this morn it is I that am the mother of a man who is among the great ones of the earth. All over the land they will be telling of Dugald Stewart. Mothers will teach their children to be men by him. High will his name be with the teller of fine tales. . . . The great men came, they came in their pride, terrible like the storm they were, and cunning with the words of guile were they. Death was with them. . . . He was but a lad, a young lad, with great length of days before him, and the grandeur of the world. But he put it all from him. "Speak," said they, "speak, and life and great riches will be for yourself." But he said no word at all! Loud was the swelling of their wrath! Let the heart of you rejoice, Morag Cameron, for the snow is red with his blood. There are things greater than death. Let them that are children shed the tears. . . .

[*She comes forward and lays her hand on the girl's shoulder.*]

Mary Stewart. Let us go and lift him into the house, and not be leaving him lie out there alone.

CURTAIN

CATHERINE PARR

BY MAURICE BARING

HENRY VIII

From a pen-drawing by
E. Heber Thompson

EDITOR'S PREFACE

Here we have King Henry VIII., old and very stout and very hot-tempered, quarrelling with the only one of his wives who contrived to outlive him. If we are not to miss the point of some of her remarks, we have to remember that the other wives were Katharine of Aragon, Anne Bullen (or Boleyn), Jane Seymour, Anne of Cleves, and Catherine Howard. We should remember, too, that Catherine Parr, like Anne of Cleves, was a Protestant, a "Lutheran," and Henry disliked Protestants, although he had broken away from the Church of Rome.

CHARACTERS

King Henry VIII.
Queen Catherine.
A Page.

CATHERINE PARR

OR

ALEXANDER'S HORSE

SCENE.—*London. Breakfast chamber in the palace. King Henry VIII. and Catherine Parr are discovered sitting opposite to each other at the breakfast table. The King has just cracked a boiled egg.*

King Henry. My egg's raw. It really is too bad.

Catherine. Yesterday you complained of their being hard.

King Henry. And so they were. I don't want a hard egg, and I don't want a raw egg. I want them to be cooked just right.

Catherine. You are very difficult to please. The egg was in boiling water for three minutes and a half. I boiled it myself. But give it me. I like them like that. I will boil you another.

King Henry. No, it's too late now. But it is a fact that you have no idea how to boil an egg. I wish you'd let them do them in the kitchen.

Catherine. If they're done in the kitchen you complain because they're not here when you come down, and if they are here, you say they're cold.

King Henry. I never say anything of the kind. The cook boils eggs beautifully.

Catherine. She shall boil them to-morrow.

King Henry. One would have thought that a woman of your experience might at least know how to boil an egg. I hate a watery egg. [*Pensively.*] Poor dear Katie used to boil eggs beautifully.

Catherine. Do you mean Catherine Howard or Katharine of Aragon?

King Henry. I was alluding to poor, dear, misguided Katie Howard. Katharine of Aragon never was my wife. The marriage was not valid.

Catherine. Well, Catherine Howard ought to have known how to boil eggs, considering her mother was a kitchenmaid.

King Henry. That is utterly untrue. Her mother was a Rochford.

Catherine. You're thinking of Anne Bullen.

King Henry. Yes, yes, to be sure, Katie's mother was a Somerset.

Catherine. You're thinking of Jane Seymour.

King Henry. Not at all. Jane Seymour was a sister of Somerset's.

Catherine. All I know is that Catherine Howard's mother was a kitchenmaid. And I think it's very unkind of you to mention her to me. I suppose you mean that you wish she were alive, and that you loved her better than you love me.

King Henry. I never said anything of the kind. All I said was that she knew how to boil eggs.

Catherine. You clearly meant to say that she had all the qualities which I lack.

King Henry. You are most unfair. I never meant to hint at any such thing. All I said was that I hate a watery egg, and my egg this morning was raw.

Catherine [*rising and going to the door in a temper*]. Well, the best thing you can do is to get rid of me, and to marry some one who knows how to boil an egg.

King Henry. Catherine, come back! I really didn't mean to offend you. You know how to boil eggs very well.

Catherine [*sitting down*]. One takes an endless amount of trouble, and that's all the thanks one gets.

Don't think that I shall ever boil your eggs for you again, because I shan't.

King Henry. I was thinking we might have a little music this morning. I have composed a new ballad which I should like to try over with you. It's for viol and lute and voice. We might try it.

Catherine. I'm not sure if I have time. What is it called?

King Henry. It's called " The Triumph of Love," and it begins:

> Come list to Alexander's deed,
> Great Jove's immortal son,
> Who, riding on a snow-white steed
> To Babylon did come.

Catherine. " Son " doesn't rhyme with " come."

King Henry. It's not meant to. It's assonance.

Catherine. Do you mean Alexander the Great?

King Henry. Yes, of course.

Catherine. The only thing is, his horse was black.

King Henry. No, my dear, you're mistaken; his horse was white.

Catherine. Black—black as jet.

King Henry. But I know for a fact it was white.

Catherine. Alexander's horse was black. Everybody knows it was black.

King Henry. It was white. You can ask any one you like.

Catherine. It was black. He was famous for his black horse. There are hundreds of pictures of him on his *black* horse—my father has got one.

King Henry. Then the painter made a mistake. Plutarch, Xenophon, Aristotle all mention his *white* horse.

Catherine. Black.

King Henry. But, my dear, how obstinate you are! I *know* it is white——

Catherine. Black, *coal*-black.

King Henry. Have you read Xenophon?

Catherine. You are thinking of something else. Even when we were children my father always showed us the picture of Alexander's *black* horse.

King Henry. Well, I can easily prove it to you. There's a Plutarch here in the bookcase.

[*He goes to the bookcase and takes out a book.*]

Catherine. I remember it particularly well, because my brother had a black horse and we called it "Bucephalus," after Alexander's *black* horse.

King Henry [*turning over the leaves of the book*]. If it had been black it would never have been called Bucephalus—it would be absurd to call a black horse Bucephalus.

Catherine. Not so absurd as calling a white horse Bucephalus.

King Henry. He would never have chosen a black horse. He was superstitious——

Catherine. Just because you're superstitious and believe in saints, and worship images, you think every one else is. As a matter of fact, he chose a black horse on purpose to show he didn't care a pin about superstitions——

King Henry. Here it is—"χαλεπὸς εἶναι καὶ κομιδῇ δύσχρηστος"—"The horse was wild and extremely difficult to manage." In fact, he had all the characteristics of the white Thessalian horses of that day.

Catherine. But it doesn't say it was white. And Thessalian horses are famous for being black.

King Henry. You really are too obstinate for words. I will find you the proofs in Xenophon. It is distinctly stated that the horse is *white*. It is an historical fact. Nobody has ever disputed it.

Catherine. But Plutarch, you see, practically says it was black.

King Henry. Plutarch says nothing of the kind. Besides, I now remember talking about this with Wolsey, who was an excellent scholar. I distinctly remember his saying one day: "As white as Bucephalus." It's quite a common phrase among scholars.

Catherine. He must have said, "As black as Bucephalus."

King Henry. Of course, if you mean to say I tell lies——

Catherine. I don't mean that you tell lies, but you are mistaken—that's all.

King Henry. But I tell you that there is no mistake possible. I know it as well as I know my own name.

Catherine. Your memory plays you tricks. Just now you couldn't remember Catherine Howard's mother's name.

King Henry. That's nothing to do with it. Besides, I did remember it. I made a slip, that's all. But this is an historical fact which I've known all my life.

Catherine. I quite understand your memory failing you. You have so many names to remember. I expect you were confusing Alexander's black horse with King Alfred's white horse—the white horse of Wantage.

King Henry. Good gracious! If you had a smattering of education you wouldn't say such things! It comes of having no religion and no education, and of not knowing Latin. A Lutheran education is worse than none. Even Anne of Cleves knew Latin.

Catherine. Thank Heavens, I don't know Latin! Stupid, superstitious language, fit only for bigots and monks!

King Henry. I suppose you mean I am a bigot.

Catherine. You can turn what one says into meaning anything you like. As a matter of fact, all I said was that the horse was black.

King Henry. I'd rather be a bigot than a Lutheran heretic.

Catherine. You know you're wrong and you try to escape the point. That's just like a Tudor. No Tudor could ever listen to reason.

King Henry. I must ask you not to insult my family.

Catherine. You've insulted mine, which is a far older one. My family has no blood on its escutcheon.

King Henry. I won't stand this any longer. [*He gets up, opens the door, and calls*] Denny, Butts, Page, who is there ?

[*Enter a Page*.]

Page. Your Majesty.

King Henry. Go and tell the Lord Chamberlain to make the necessary arrangements for transporting the Ex-Queen to the Tower.

Page [*puzzled*]. Yes, your Majesty. Does your Majesty mean the late Queen's remains ?

King Henry. I said the *Ex*-Queen, you stupid boy —Queen Catherine Parr.

Page. Yes, your Majesty.

King Henry. And tell him to give orders to the Governor of the Tower to have everything ready for the Ex-Queen's execution.

Page. Is the same ceremonial to be observed as in the case of Queen Catherine Howard, your Majesty ?

King Henry. Yes ; only there need only be one roll of drums instead of two—at the end. [*The Page goes to the door*.] And on the way ask Dr. Butts whether Alexander the Great's horse was black or white.

Catherine. It was black. [*The Page bows and goes out*.] Well, since I'm to be executed, I daresay you will allow me to go and pack up my things. By the way, you left your lute in my sitting-room yesterday. I will bring it down.

King Henry. Wait a minute, there's no hurry.

Catherine. I beg your pardon, I have very little time, and a great many letters to write.

King Henry [*hesitating*]. And I wanted to have some music.

Catherine. You don't expect me to accompany you now, I suppose ? You had better find some one else.

I have got other things to think about during my last moments on earth.

King Henry [*laughing uneasily*]. I was only joking, of course, my dear. You don't mean to say you took it seriously.

Catherine. I am afraid I don't appreciate that kind of joke.

King Henry. Come, come; let bygones be bygones, and let us have some music. I want to play you my ballad.

[*Enter the Page.*]

Page. If you please, your Majesty, I can't find the Lord Chamberlain, and Dr. Butts says your Majesty was quite correct as to the colour of Alexander the Great's horse.

King Henry [*beaming*]. Very good; you can go. You need not deliver the message to the Lord Chamberlain. [*The Page bows and retires.*] And now, my dear, we'll go and play. You see, I knew I was right.

[*The King opens the door with a bow.*]

Catherine. It was black, all the same.

King Henry [*indulgently, as if speaking to a child*]. Yes, yes, my dear, of course it was black, but let's go and have some music. [*They go out.*]

CURTAIN

MICHAEL

BY MILES MALLESON

CHARACTERS

Michael was first produced by the students of the Academy of Dramatic Art on Tuesday, April 3, 1917, at the St. James's Theatre, with the following cast:

SIMON	Miss Phyllis Hiller.
MATRYONA	Miss Joan Allen.
ANIUSKA	Miss Noreen Price.
MICHAEL	Miss Gabrielle Clay.
A RUSSIAN NOBLE	Miss Kitty Penberthy.
HIS SERVANT	Miss Phyllis Fenton.
A WOMAN	Miss Molly Wood.
TWO CHILDREN	Miss May Taylor. Miss Ellen Bird.

The play is adapted from the translation by L. and A. Maude of Tolstoy's story, *What Men Live By*.

MICHAEL

SCENE I

A Russian peasant hut. The door into the open air is in the centre of the back wall; there is another door into an inner room on the right as one looks on to the stage. The fireplace is opposite on the left, with a rough wooden bench by it. The room is barely furnished. There is a wooden table and a few wooden stools. On the table are a few tattered clothes and some sewing materials.

An empty stage at the rise of the curtain. A peasant woman enters from out of doors carrying a water-pail. She crosses to look into the inner room, evidently finds it empty, and calls:

Matryona. Aniuska . . . Aniuska! [*A child's voice answers from outside in a loud happy* Oo . . . ee. *The woman crosses to the door and calls out into the open.*] Bring in those sticks you gathered, Aniuska; bring them in for the fire. Now. Now, at once.

[*She returns to the fireplace and for a moment busies herself there. An enormous collection of sticks makes its appearance at the door. The collection begins to advance into the room uneasily and uncannily, and apparently on two little bare feet of its own. However, a child is seen to be supplying the motive power. The sticks are deposited by the fireplace.*]

Matryona. Now make up the fire with them,

Aniuska. Your father will be back soon from the town.

[*The child squats on the floor and begins to break up the sticks. The little ones are easy enough, but she has some hard tussles with the stouter ones. She is busy thus through the following scene. Matryona seats herself at the table and begins to patch a very ragged shirt.*]

Aniuska. Woof! [*A stick is broken at that.*] Mummy—woof——.

Matryona. Yes?

Aniuska. Woof! Why has daddy gone into the town?

Matryona. To buy a warm sheepskin for the winter. We've only one between us, and that's worn to tatters.

Aniuska. Woof! Why doesn't daddy—woof!—go into the town and buy warm sheepskins more often . . . woof! . . . I can't ever remember daddy having been away for the whole day before. . . .

Matryona. There's never a moment to be spared from his work.

Aniuska. Woof!

Matryona. Work's cheap, but bread's dear; and what he earns goes on food; there's little use tramping many weary miles to the town with no money to spend.

Aniuska. Woof! . . . Has daddy got some money now?

Matryona. Little enough. It's taken a year—day in and day out, making boots for the neighbours, to save enough for one sheepskin. And he's got to collect most of it on his way to the town.

Aniuska. Who's he going to collect it from?

Matryona. From the neighbours he's made boots for, silly. [*Matryona continues musing half to herself and half to the child.*] If only the dealer doesn't cheat him—he's much too simple—he cheats nobody, but any child can take him in . . . eight roubles is a lot

Rouble, A coin which was worth about half-a-crown.

of money. He should get a good coat at that price. Not tanned skin, but still, a proper winter coat. It'll be better this winter than last. When he went out he put on our one coat, and I had to stay indoors.

Aniuska [*after a tremendous but vain struggle with a too thick piece of stick*]. Nasty, nasty, nasty, nasty! I can't "woof" it!

Matryona. Tell me how much bread there is, Aniuska. . . . He'll be wanting something when he comes back. [*The child goes to a cupboard and holds up a piece of bread.*] That'll have to do. He'll have had some dinner in the town. Set it out, Aniuska. [*She takes her sewing from the table to the bench by the fire. Aniuska sets out the bread and a bowl or two, dancing and skipping to and fro between the table and the cupboard—singing a little to herself. Matryona continues*] He didn't start very early. It's a long way, and he had to collect the money on his way, but it's time he was back—I only hope he hasn't gone on the spree.

Aniuska [*having set out her father's meal, she has gone to the door. Suddenly*]. Here he comes! Here comes daddy! [*In tremendous excitement she rushes to her mother and then back to the door to run out to meet him; but instead, she stops short.*] Daddy isn't alone. There's somebody with him.

Matryona. What's that? What sort of a person with him? [*She puts away her work.*]

Aniuska. He must be terribly cold, his arms are all bare, and his feet . . . He looks like a beggar.

Matryona. A beggar!

Aniuska. No. He doesn't look like a beggar.

Matryona. Has your father a sheepskin?

Aniuska. No.

Matryona. No sheepskin! [*She hurries to the door.*] No sheepskin! Nothing! And bringing a beggar home with him. It's as I feared. He's been on the spree. It's vodka the money's gone on, and

Vodka, An intoxicating drink, distilled from rye.

not a sheepskin. [*Her temper begins to rise quickly.*] Here's a nice end to a year's work. My heart could break with disappointment. A year's savings on a drunken spree. [*She vents her rising anger on the child.*] Get off to bed!

Aniuska [*extremely plaintive*]. I want to see daddy.

Matryona. Off with you! You don't see your father drunk—and you don't hear what I've got to say to him! Off with you!

Aniuska [*her voice quivering with tears*]. I haven't seen daddy all day.

Matryona. Off with you—and put yourself into your bed. [*Aniuska, her knuckles stuffed into her eyes in an ineffectual attempt to keep back her tears, goes slowly into the inner room. Matryona shuts the door after her, and then shuts the door into the open air. She begins to work herself up into a passionate indignation.*] Oh, it's a nice end to it. One slaves and slaves and slaves, and the money goes on drink, and he brings his good-for-nothing drunken friends home with him. Well, we shall see!

[*She takes up her stand by the fireplace and waits. The door is opened. Simon comes in. He holds the door open for some one else.*]

Simon. Come in, friend. . . . Come in.

[*A young man, apparently of about eighteen, enters. His face is beautiful and his bare limbs wonderfully shaped. Just a piece of coarse material wound round him, and Simon's old cloak across his shoulders, keep out the cold as best they may. Having entered, he stands just inside the door, his head and eyes lowered. Simon is not at all the worse for drink, but evidently very anxious about his reception by his wife.*]

Simon. Well, mother? [*She does not answer.*] Come, friend. Here by the fire. Sit and warm yourself. [*He sets the bench nearer to the fire, and beckons the stranger to it.*] There! That's better than the snow outside! We'll have some supper. Any supper for us, mother?

Matryona. You shall have your supper when I have my sheepskin.

Simon. Oh, come, mother—that's a poor welcome! I couldn't get the skin.

Matryona. Why not?

Simon. I called on neighbour Trifonof on my way to the town, but he couldn't pay me what he owed. He hadn't the money. Hardly enough bread for his wife and children. I couldn't force him. I went on and asked the dealers to let me have a skin on credit, but they wouldn't—so we must go without.

Matryona. Where's the money that you started with?

Simon. Here. [*He gives her some.*]

Matryona [*counting it*]. It's not all.

Simon. I spent some.

Matryona. On what?

Simon. On vodka.

Matryona. So! That's what I thought.

Simon. Just enough to keep out the cold. Many miles through the snow—like this—it's cold work . . . and hungry work, too.

Matryona. There's no supper for drunkards like you.

Simon. Now then, mother.

Matryona. Maybe the cold's sobered you. But you set out to buy a sheepskin, and you come back with nothing but a naked vagabond.

Simon. That's enough, Matryona. Don't wag your tongue without reason. . . .

Matryona. And you ask for supper! As if nothing had happened. There's only enough bread in the house for a day—we can't feed all the drunkards in the country.

Simon. There now, Matryona, hold your tongue.

Matryona. Hold my tongue indeed! Yes. I've finished with you. You expect me to slave for another year, do you? Then you can get your own supper—and mind your own house. . . . Here, give that to me! [*She seizes the cloak from the stranger's shoulders and throws it round her. She goes to the door, but neither her husband nor the stranger move, and her curiosity is roused. She comes back and addresses the stranger.*] If you haven't been on a drunken spree, how came you like that? [*No answer.*] You must be a bad man—you're afraid. [*No answer; and she draws a little nearer to him.*] You're clothed like a beggar, but your skin is white and your hands are smooth. . . . Where do you come from? . . . What do you want? [*The stranger shakes his head.*] Haven't you a tongue in your head?

Simon. He hasn't spoken a word since I found him.

Matryona. Found him? Where did you find him?

Simon. By the roadside. I was passing a shrine at a bend of the road, and I saw something on the ground against it, and when I went closer I found him—naked in the snow. I thought some one must have stripped him and left him there, and if I meddled I should get into trouble—so I hurried on. . . . And then I thought he might be dying of cold and want, and I was slipping past—afraid! "Simon," I said to myself, "have you grown so rich as to be afraid of robbers? Shame on you!" So I went back, and lifted him up, and put my cloak round him and brought him home. I questioned him, but he never spoke. . . . And now you know as much as I.

[*Matryona regards him still more curiously.*]

Matryona. His skin's as white and soft as a nobleman's. In the snow like that! It's a wonder he's alive! Well, we can't let him starve. Here! Out of my way! [*Her voice is kinder. She wishes to reach a kettle on the fire.*] Here . . . sit here. You'll be warmer here. [*She sets a chair for him nearer the fire so that she can reach the kettle. His back is now to the audience. She fills a cup and gives it to him.*] There.

Drink that. That'll warm you. [*He looks up at her when he takes it ; and suddenly, drawing a little back, she stares at him. As if spellbound and unable to take her eyes from the stranger, she gets closer to Simon. Her voice is full of awed fear.*] Did you see. . . . Simon . . . did you see ?

Simon. What was there to see, mother ?

Matryona. When I handed him the cup, he smiled at me. The strangest smile I've ever seen ! I've never seen a man smile like that. He smiled as if the sun were behind his eyes. Simon, I'm afraid. . . . I'm afraid of him . . . there's something very strange.

Simon. Strange or not—as you say, we can't let him starve. Give him the bread.

Matryona. You.

Simon. Here, friend, take this.

[*Simon gives him the bread. For a moment they both watch him. Then :*]

Matryona. And that's the last food in the house, and you'll be wanting some. Perhaps I can borrow a little from neighbour Martha—I'll go across now. [*By the door she hesitates.*] It's very dark. The stranger's put a spell on me—I'm fearing to go across the black field. . . . Come with me, Simon. He'll be well enough for a while. [*Simon joins her at the door.*] We'd best take the lantern.

Simon. No, mother. We know every step of the way. . . . Take my hand.

[*They go out together. The stranger sits silent on the bench. From the inner room the child's voice calls :*]

Aniuska. Mother . . . Mother . . . Daddy . . . Dad-*dy* . . .

[*The child appears in a tiny little white shirt ; she peeps out into the room. Then she advances into it. When she sees the stranger, she observes him in surprised silence. Slowly she crosses the room to him. He looks up, and she stands taking him in with a solemn, fearless curiosity. She accepts him and gives him a hand, which he takes. Then, climbing up on to his lap, she rests her head contentedly against his shoulder. The stage becomes black.*]

SCENE II

In a few moments it is light again.

The same Scene. A year has elapsed. Simon sits shoemaking. Matryona is sewing.

Matryona. Simon.

Simon. Yes, mother?

Matryona. Do you know what to-day is?

Simon. No. What is to-day?

Matryona. It's a year ago since you brought Michael home.

Simon. The luckiest day's work I ever did. Never did I know a man take so readily to his work, or so easy to teach as Michael. And now no one sews boots so neatly and strongly in all the district. His fame is beginning to spread, too. People are coming a long way to have their boots sewn here. We shall soon be well off.

Matryona. And yet from that day to this, he's still as great a mystery as ever. Where is he now?

Simon. He's but taken some boots to a neighbour.

Matryona. It's seldom his bench there is empty. He seems to work without stopping—silently. It is strange. He only speaks when necessary, and he does not joke nor laugh. And—except once, except that once—I have never seen him smile. Do you know, father, I often think something very strange will happen, and we shall lose him.

Simon. God put off the day! He's too good a workman.

[*The door opens, and Michael in peasant dress appears.*

He comes in, and going silently to his bench, begins to work. They have only worked a few moments when the bells of a carriage-sledge are heard outside. Matryona goes at once to the door.]

Matryona. Oh, what a carriage! And beautiful horses, and servants! It must belong to a great nobleman . . . it's stopping . . . the servants are getting down . . . the nobleman! . . . he's getting out . . . he's coming here. [*She shuts the door in alarm.*] Simon, a great nobleman is coming up our pathway!

[*Simon rises, and they wait anxiously. Michael works on unconcerned. There is an imperious knock at the door. Matryona opens it timidly. A magnificently dressed noble swaggers in.*]

Nobleman. Are you the master bootmaker?

Simon. I am, your Excellency.

Nobleman [*calling from the door*]. Fedka, bring the leather. . . . [*A servant runs in with some leather.*] Give it to me. . . . Look here, shoemaker. Do you see this leather?

Simon. Yes, your Excellency.

Nobleman. Do you know what sort of leather it is?

Simon. It is good leather.

Nobleman. Good indeed! Why, you fool, you never saw such leather before in your life. It's foreign. It cost me twenty roubles.

Simon [*aghast*]. Twenty roubles! Where should I ever see leather like that?

Nobleman. Just so. Now, can you make it into boots for me?

Simon. Yes, your Excellency, I can.

Nobleman. You can, can you? Well, remember whom you are to make them for, and what the leather is. You must make me boots that will wear for a year, neither losing shape nor coming unsewn. If you can do it, take the leather and cut it up—but if you can't, you'd better say so. I warn you now, if you spoil my leather, I will have you put in prison.

Simon. Your Excellency!

Nobleman. But if you make good boots, as I want them, I will pay you ten roubles for your work. Will you do it?

Simon. Ten roubles. . . .

Nobleman. Ten roubles. . . . Well?

Simon. . . . Yes, your Excellency, I will do it.

Nobleman. Very well. Take my measure. [*The Nobleman sits so that his own servant can remove one of his boots. Simon begins to take the measure.*] Mind you don't make it too tight!

Simon. No, your Excellency.

[*Aniuska comes skipping, bounding, shouting into the room, unaware of the Nobleman.*]

Matryona [*terrified that such a hullabaloo will annoy the Nobleman*]. Aniuska!

[*The child sees the Nobleman, is overcome, and creeps to hide her head in her mother's skirts.*]

Nobleman. Is that yours?

Matryona. Yes, your Excellency.

[*The measure has been taken, and the Nobleman rises.*]

Nobleman. There! And take care, for your own sake, my leather is not spoiled. [*He notices Michael, who has been working unconcerned.*] Whom have we here?

Simon. That is my workman—he will sew the boots.

Nobleman. Oh, he will sew them, will he? [*He swaggers across to Michael.*] Mind! Remember to make them so that they will last a year. They must neither lose shape nor come unsewn.

[*Michael rises slowly from his seat. His back is to the audience. He stands gazing towards the Nobleman. Matryona seizes Simon by the arm.*]

Matryona [*whispering*]. Simon! Look! Look at Michael! Michael's face! He's smiling!

Simon [*under his breath*]. God protect us!

Matryona. . . . As he did when he looked at me a year ago.

Nobleman [*in loud uneasiness*]. . . . What are you grinning at, you fool? Stop! Stop grinning! [*He advances to him threateningly; but as Michael does not move, the Nobleman hesitates, then turns to the door.*] Instead of standing there smiling, if you take my advice you'll sew my boots as I want them, and earn ten roubles for your master. But if the leather's spoiled, you grinning fool, there's prison for you as well as him. Come, Fedka.

[*The Nobleman and his servant go out. Michael stands unmoving, and Simon and his wife watch him, strangely fascinated.*]

Simon [*recalled by the leather*]. It's wonderful leather. You must cut it, Michael—and take care how you cut. If the leather's spoilt, it's ruin for us all. There! [*He gives him the leather with the greatest care.*] Wait now till I give you the measure. [*He turns to fetch the measure.*] Your eye is truer than mine—you must cut as you never cut before, and cut exact.

[*But without waiting for the measure Michael folds the leather and cuts it boldly into two pieces.*]

Simon [*in a terrible state*]. Michael! For God's sake! What have you done? [*Michael deliberately cuts it again.*] The leather's spoiled. O God! We're ruined! We shall be taken off to the prison! Matryona, Aniuska—little one—our home will be broken up!—the nobleman will be enraged, and we shall be helpless against him. . . . Michael, never before have you made a mistake, and now your mistake has ruined us all! [*He examines what Michael has done.*] It's spoiled—utterly spoiled! Oh, mother, mother, we're ruined! No boots could in any way be cut from that now—only soft slippers!

[*The servant of the Nobleman bursts back into the room. He is very excited.*]

Servant. I have been sent back about the boots.

Simon. About the boots.

Servant. My master no longer needs them.

Simon [*repeating slowly*]. Your master no longer needs them ?

Servant. He is dead ! . . . Hardly had he rejoined his lady in the sledge and we'd started off, the horses had been whipped into a gallop, and we were flying across the snow, when we heard a great cry from our mistress for us to stop . . . and before we could get down and go to him, he was dead. The life was out of him and he rolled over on to the floor of the carriage, like a sack. . . . My mistress has sent me back. I am to tell you there is no longer any need for the boots, but you are to use the leather to make soft slippers for the corpse.

Simon [*slowly, incredulously*]. Soft slippers for the corpse ? . . .

Servant. I shall return for them to-morrow. Good-day, masters. [*Exit.*]

Simon. Soft slippers for the corpse ! . . .

[*Simon and Matryona stare at Michael, who sits down and commences work on the slippers. The stage becomes black.*]

SCENE III

The light goes up again in a moment on a busy scene. It is towards evening. Michael and Simon are at work. Aniuska, on the floor, is engrossed with her toys—a number of rough, but brilliantly painted wooden ones. Matryona moves to and fro ceaselessly, busied on household tasks.

A timid knock at the door. The work in the room stops—the knock is repeated a little louder.

Simon. It's late for customers.

Matryona. See who it is, Aniuska.

[*The child opens the door. Whoever it was outside has gone a few steps away, and Aniuska disappears. In a moment she is back again.*]

Aniuska. There's a lady with two little girls, and one of them has a bad leg.

[*Michael's attention has been caught—he rises from his bench. A woman appears in the doorway. She has two little girls with her, of whom one is lame. Michael is evidently deeply moved by them.*]

Woman. Good-evening, good folk.

Simon. Good-evening to you.

Woman. I have come about some shoes for these little girls.

Simon. Pray come in. What sort of shoes do you want ?

Woman. I want leather shoes made for them for the spring.

Simon. We can do that. Welted or turned over, linen-lined. My man Michael is a master at the work.

[*Michael has continued to stare at the two little girls excitedly. Realizing now that all eyes are on him he shrinks back into the shadow.*]

Woman. Will you take the measure now ?

Simon. Yes.

Woman [*lifting the lame child on to her lap*]. Take the two measures from this little girl. Make one shoe for the lame foot and three for the sound one, and two pairs for the other little girl. They both have the same-sized shoes—they are twins.

Simon [*as he takes the measurement*]. How did it happen to her ? She is such a pretty little girl. Was she born so ?

Woman. No. Her mother crushed her leg.

Matryona. Aren't you their mother, then ?

Woman. No. I am neither their mother nor any relation to them. They were quite strangers to me, but I adopted them.

Matryona. They are not your children, and yet you are so fond of them ?

Woman. How can I help being fond of them ? I fed

them both—I had a child of my own, but God took him. I was not so fond of him as I am now of these.

Matryona. Whose children are they ?

[*Aniuska has made friends with the other little girl and has taken her to the toys. As soon as the measurement is taken the lame child joins them, and on the floor the three play together.*

The daylight is fading, and the light in the room has grown very dim. There is a lamp on the table which sheds its soft light on the group round it ; but the shadows outside the circle are very deep and black ; Michael in his far corner cannot be seen.]

Woman. Their parents died both in one week. My husband and I lived in the same village. Their father was a lonely man—a woodcutter in the forest. When felling trees one day they let one fall on him. It fell across his body and crushed him. They hardly got him home before he died ; and that same week his wife gave birth to these two little girls. She was poor and alone, she had no one, young or old, with her, and alone she met her death. The next morning I went to see her, but when I entered the hut, poor thing, she was already stark and cold. In dying she had rolled on to one of the children and crushed its leg. The village folk came to the hut, washed the body, laid her out, made a coffin, and buried her. They were good folk. The babies were left alone. What was to be done with them ? I was the only woman there who had a baby at the time, and so I fed my own boy—and these two . . . and God so ordered it, that these grew up, while my own was buried before he was two years old. I had no more children of my own, and how lonely I should be without these two little girls ! How can I help loving them ! They are the joy of my life. . . . [*She rises and watches the children playing on the floor.*] And what a beautiful little one you have ! [*She turns to Matryona.*] We are very lucky. . . . Come, little ones, say good-bye, it's late—we should be back.

[*She helps up the lame one.*]

Matryona. You are not from these parts ?

Woman. No. We are staying with a neighbour. They told me to come to you for the shoes. They will be ready soon ?

Simon. In two days.

Woman. Thank you, and good-night.

Simon [*opening the door for her*]. Good-night to you.

Matryona. It's dark. Do you know the way ?

Woman. When I get on to the pathway.

Matryona. Simon, show the way. It's rough for the little one. . . . Good-bye, little ones. [*She kisses the two little girls.*] Come back to get your shoes and play again with Aniuska.

Aniuska. Can I go with daddy ?

Matryona. Down to the pathway. . . . Hey, but it's dark ! Perhaps this will light the way.

[*Matryona takes the lamp from the table and carries it to the doorway. There she stands with it, high above her head, to light the others down the pathway. She waves good-bye ; then she herself, still with the lamp, disappears out of doors. Inside the room it is dark. Then, from the corner in which Michael was, a strange light begins to shine. The light grows gradually brighter until Michael is seen clearly in the midst of it.*

Matryona comes back into the room. She goes straight to the table, upon which she replaces the lamp. She does not see Michael until she turns. Then :]

Matryona [*her voice low with awe and fear*]. Simon ! . . . Simon ! . . . [*Simon, with Aniuska, comes back into the room.*]

Simon. . . . God protect us ! . . .

Matryona. . . . Michael is smiling . . . I cannot bear to look !

Simon [*in low awe*]. Michael . . . Michael, we are afraid before you; we do not know, and we are afraid. Only tell me this: why does your face shine so?

Michael. Light shines from me because I have been punished, and now I am forgiven.

Simon. And why do you smile so, and why have you smiled so, these three times?

Michael. I smiled three times, because I was sent to learn three truths, and I have learnt them. . . . One I learned when your wife pitied me, and that is why I smiled the first time. The second I learned when the rich man ordered the boots, and I smiled the second time, and now I have learnt the third truth, and I smiled the third time.

Simon [*with low reverence*]. Tell me, Michael, what were you punished for? And what were the three truths? That I, too, may know them.

Michael. I was an angel in heaven, and disobeyed. [*The three figures, of Simon, of Matryona, and Aniuska, can be seen dimly, in a little group, by the light of the lamp on the table: its light seems to burn very low and small beside the great light round Michael. Matryona is seen to kneel, and the child, observing, kneels too.*] God sent me to fetch a woman's soul. I flew to earth and saw a sick woman lying alone, who had just given birth to two little girls. When she saw me she understood, and she wept and said, "Angel of God! My husband has just been buried—killed by a falling tree. There is no one to care for my babes and set them on their feet before I die. Children cannot live without father or mother."

And I hearkened to her. And I flew to the Lord and said: "Her husband has just been killed, and she has two new-born babes; I have not taken her soul." And God said: "Go, take the mother's soul, and learn three truths. Learn: WHAT DWELLS IN MAN; WHAT IS NOT GIVEN TO MAN; and, WHAT MEN LIVE BY.

When thou hast learnt these three things thou shalt return to heaven."

So I flew again to earth, and took the mother's soul. Her body rolled over and crushed one babe, twisting its leg. I rose above the village, but a wind seized me, and my wings drooped and dropt. Her soul rose alone, while I fell to earth, by the roadside. . . . Never before had I known human needs, but then I was hungry, frozen, and in pain. Suddenly I heard a man coming along the road. [*A movement from Simon. He is seen to be listening with the most intense excitement.*] For the first time since I became a man, I saw the mortal face of a man. And when he saw me he frowned, and seemed terrible to me, and he passed me by on the other side. [*A low cry escapes Simon. He is seen to sink his head into his hands, bowing before the angel.*] I despaired. Suddenly I heard him coming back. I looked up and did not recognize the same man. Before, I had seen death in his face, but now he was alive, and I recognized in him the presence of God. [*Simon is seen to raise his head, and hold himself up straight again.*] He took me to his home—a woman was there. [*The kneeling Matryona is seen to sink low to the ground.*] She was still more terrible than the man had been : the spirit of death came from her ; I could not breathe for the stench of death that spread around her. She wished to drive me out into the cold, and I knew that if she did so, she would die. [*A low cry comes from Matryona.*] But suddenly she changed ; she brought me food, and when I looked at her I saw that Death no longer dwelt in her ; she had become alive, and in her, too, I saw God. And I remembered my first lesson : "LEARN WHAT DWELLS IN MAN." And I understood that in man dwells Love—and I smiled the first time.

A year passed. A man came to order boots that should wear for a year. And I saw behind his shoulder my comrade, the Angel of Death. And I knew before the sun set he would take the rich man's soul. And I remembered my second lesson: "LEARN WHAT IS NOT GIVEN TO MAN." It is not given to man to know his own needs—and I smiled the second time.

A year passed. And there came the girl-children with the woman; and I heard how they had been kept alive, and I knew that I had learned the third truth —and I smiled the third time. . . . [*The angel's voice begins to ring with a splendid triumph.*) . . . I have learnt that all men live, not by care for themselves, but by Love. I remained alive, when I was a man, not by care of myself, but because Love was present in a passer-by and because he and his wife pitied and loved me. The orphans remained alive, not because of their mother's care, but because there was Love in the heart of a woman—a stranger, who pitied and loved them. . . . It seems to men that they live by care of themselves, but in truth it is Love alone by which they live. [*The angel's arms are stretched out and up.*] I have learnt my third lesson: "WHAT MEN LIVE BY"—it is Love alone by which they live.

[*Suddenly there is complete darkness. . . . Then, when the light of the lamp seems to steal back into the room, Simon, Matryona, and Aniuska are alone in the cottage.*]

CURTAIN

COMMENTARY

A. A. MILNE: THE PRINCESS AND THE WOODCUTTER

Mr. A. A. Milne is a dramatist of note, a contributor to *Punch*, and the author of *When We Were Very Young*, so it is not surprising that when he sets out to make fun of all the fairy-tale plays it is good fun and very light-hearted. One of the reasons why people enjoy reading his books and seeing his plays—and they do—is that he so obviously enjoys writing them.

Now we daren't be solemn about *The Princess and the Woodcutter*, partly because it would be silly, and partly because Mr. Milne might make us into a joke in *Punch*. To be made into a joke in *Punch* is the height of fame, it means that you really are some one important at last—but it has its drawbacks.

However, we may look through the play again, to make sure that we have not missed any of the smiles, and afterwards, if you can, you should read the whole of *Make-Believe* (of which play this is Act I.); if you have any doubts as to whether the love-making of the Princess and the Woodcutter is quite the right thing, you should at least be satisfied with the pirates and cannibals in Act II.

ON TALKING IT OVER

1. Seven-headed bulls have gone out of fashion, but evidently they had their uses. How did this one help

with the suitors? And how did he die?—the Princess is still unmarried!

2. What *is* the Red Prince like?

3. At which point do you feel that the Yellow Prince ought to be kicked (or smacked)?

4. What do you think of, "*amazed, as well he may be*"? (page 28).

5. The author enjoys his stage-directions as much as his dialogue. Which of the directions do you like best?

FOR PEN AND PENCIL

6. If you have anticipated the advice of the Princess and ' read the history books," you know the stories in which the poor miller's son kills the fiery dragon which has eaten all the Princess's suitors, and then marries the Princess; and the little kitchen-wench wins the handsome prince, while the ugly daughters of her cruel stepmother are all turned into centipedes or something equally unpleasant. They are good stories, and some of them are very old, and some—if we may be almost solemn for a moment, in the hope that Mr. Milne is not looking—are known all over the world; they are told in Eskimo huts under the flickering northern lights; and repeated by the story-teller to his little crowd of listeners at street corners in Persian bazaars; and laughed at by sunburnt boys and girls in the shade of the palm-trees on far Pacific islands.

Choose a fairy-tale or a folk-tale or a legend, and make it into a play, either seriously or in imitation of Mr. Milne. If you do not know a story that will do, you will find ample choice in *Stories from the Arabian Nights*, or *Folk-Tales of the Nations*, or *Tales from Hans Andersen and Grimm*; they are all in this Series.

7. Draw and paint a brightly-coloured frontispiece for *The Princess and the Woodcutter*.

BOOKS TO READ

8. *Make-Believe*, a three-act play; *The Boy Comes Home*, and *The Man in the Bowler Hat*, one-act plays, by A. A. Milne.

Peter Pan and Wendy, by J. M. Barrie.
Twice is Too Much, in *Pattern Plays*, by Mary Oakden and E. C. Sturt (T.E.S.).

ALFRED NOYES: ROBIN HOOD

Some historians tell us nowadays that Robin Hood never existed, but whether he lived in the twelfth century or not, we know that he is very much alive now, in the immortal company of Peter Pan and Sherlock Holmes, Long John Silver, Bill Sykes, and Sam Weller, the Pied Piper, Robinson Crusoe, King Arthur, and all the other heroes of story and legend whom we know better than many of our everyday acquaintances. So Robin Hood and his outlaws live merrily in Sherwood Forest near Nottingham, robbing the rich and helping the poor, outwitting the sheriff and defying Prince John, who is ruling England very badly while his famous brother, King Richard I., is away on a crusade against the Saracens in Palestine.

Many stories of Robin Hood have been written, and now Mr. Alfred Noyes has given us a five-act play about him, in which all the well-known characters appear, besides Shadow-of-a-Leaf—a fool who is very wise and brave. The play ends with the death of Robin and Marian, but the ending is not sad, because it is full of beauty and hope. In this book we have only Act III. of the play, but it is sufficiently complete in itself to be read or acted separately.

Mr. Alfred Noyes is well known as a poet. You will probably find some of his short poems in your school poetry-books, and later on you may have a chance to read his longer poems, such as *Tales of the Mermaid Tavern.*

ON TALKING IT OVER

9. What do the words *prologue* and *epilogue* mean? In what way are they alike? How do they differ?

What do you think the separate halves of the words mean ?

10. Some verses from Mr. Noyes's poem *Sherwood* have been given in this book, as a Prologue to his play. The whole poem is in *Mount Helicon, The Golden Book of Modern English Poetry,* and other anthologies. Find it and read it all, or ask your teacher to read it, and then choose a few verses from it to form another Prologue. Can you make an Epilogue in the same way ?

11. What was a maypole ?

12. Why does the Knight wear a red cross on his shield? What does the red cross stand for nowadays ? Has this any connection with its old meaning ?

13. Why does Robin say that his name *was* Huntingdon ?

14. What do you think Jenny means by calling Widow Scarlet " a mumping mumble-crust " ?

15. Who was Mahound ? Where did the Knight learn to swear by him ?

16. Why does Prince John mutter, ' What ? Thou ? Thou ? Or his ghost ? "

17. What is a visor ?

18. Why does Robin Hood refer to Friar Tuck's " slim waist " ?

19. Note that Robin describes the venison as " borrowed from the King," because all the deer in Sherwood were the King's property. Killing them without permission was a crime punishable by death.

20. What were gauntlets, and why should they prevent the Knight from drinking the toast ?

21. Why should Robin think that a Red Cross Knight might be St. George ?

22. Can you suggest the idea which Shadow-of-a-Leaf has in his mind when he cries, " The King, the King comes home from the Crusade . . . " ?

23. Which do you think is the most exciting moment in the play ?

24. Are Robin and Marian well matched ? If so, why ?

25. Can you suggest a good title for each scene ?

26. What would be the chief difficulties in staging this play if your form were acting it, and how would you overcome them ?

FOR PEN AND PENCIL

27. Describe briefly how you would arrange a small stage for a performance of *Robin Hood.*

28. Write in rhyming verse *either* an Epilogue to the play *or* a song for Friar Tuck to sing in praise of life in Sherwood Forest.

29. Write a short dialogue between Friar Tuck and Little John, in which the Friar tells Little John (who, we will say, was not present) how Will Scarlet was rescued.

30. Write a short story or a one-act play about Robin Hood. If you don't know any of his adventures and can't make one up, then take the story of the archery tournament which the sheriff gave at Nottingham. Robin went in disguise and won the tournament, but when he went to receive his prize he was recognized by the sheriff, who ordered his guards to arrest the outlaw. Thereupon all Robin's men, who were in disguise among the crowd of spectators, came to the rescue—fully armed and in overwhelming numbers. This play should be in one scene only. You have to invent the ending and all the details.

31. Make a careful drawing of a bow, an arrow, and a quiver, and find out what they were made of.* (You must refer to a history book or an encyclopædia for this.)

32. Find a picture of Robin Hood, or Richard I., or a knight of the time in full armour, and copy it.

BOOKS TO READ

33. *Robin Hood,* a play in five acts, by Alfred Noyes. (Blackwood, 5s.)

The Greenwood, edited by Sir Henry Newbolt. (Tales of Robin Hood and English woodland life.) *Robin Hood and Alan-a-dale,* in *Pattern Plays,* by E. C. Oakden and

* It is assumed that some books, such as the following, are available in the school library: *Social England,* edited by H. D. Traill. Cassell, 6 vols., out of print. *A History of Everyday Things in England,* by M. and C. H. B. Quennell, Batsford, 16s. *Costume and Fashion,* by Herbert Norris, Dent, Vol. I., 25s., Vol. II., 31s. 6d. Others to follow. All these books are well illustrated.

Mary Sturt. Both volumes are in the "Teaching of English Series."

Robin Hood and the Pedlar. A play by John Drinkwater. (Sidgwick and Jackson.)

W. GRAHAM ROBERTSON: THE SLIPPERS OF CINDERELLA

It was not because suitable plays were not to be found that Mr. Graham Robertson wrote his own plays for young actors. "I came across suitable plays by the score," he writes in the Foreword to *The Slippers of Cinderella*, "plays good and bad, comic and tragic, but all of a uniform and depressing suitability.

"Of what interest to my volcanic leading lady, a strong, emotional actress rising ten and already with an eye on Lady Macbeth, were the pastoral but puny woes of Little Bo-Peep? What in common had my elegantly fastidious Jeune Premier of eight with Tommy Tucker or Little Jack Horner, whose table manners had long since caused him to drop their acquaintance? All had left the nursery far, far behind, from the youngest extra lady to the veteran tottering soberly into her teens, and their point of view seemed identical with that of the adult Thespian.

"What they wanted was an unsuitable play, and they looked to me to provide one; a play that should be neither idyllic, infantine, nor improving. Hang it all—as the troupe very naturally felt—why improvement?

"Hence therefore the Theatre of the Children's Troupe, of which the three following plays are specimens. Their general tone is low, their language unrefined, they contain no elements of poetry or morality, they could not by any possibility improve anybody; in a word, they can be confidently recommended to juvenile actors as entirely and absolutely unsuitable."

ON TALKING IT OVER

34. What picture of Elise had you formed before she appeared?

35. Why is Agatha so "eager" about Lady Errington, and so anxious that the right cards should be to the top in the card plate?

36. Why should Dolly now understand the feelings of Balaam? You probably remember that Balaam's ass turned suddenly and spoke to him. (*Numbers*, chap. xxii.)

37. Why should the Fairy think that the twins must be "ugly and cruel, doubtless"?

38. Which is Belinda's most amusing remark?

39. If you don't know what homœopathic means, look it up in a dictionary.

40. What do you think of Jane's plan for keeping the police busy?

41. Is Belinda right about the appointment?

42. Do you like Agatha?

43. The charm of this play is due not only to the humorous plot and witty dialogue, but (in spite of the "Foreword") to its touch of poetry. Which speech would you choose as the best instance of this?

44. As only a few fortunate people can work magic on the stage, one of the author's chief problems in writing the play must have been to arrange for Myra and Jane and Agatha to change their dresses. How has he solved the problem?

45. Why is *The Slippers of Cinderella* such a good title for the play?

FOR PEN AND PENCIL

46. Imagine that Jane is telling a friend of hers all about these extraordinary happenings, and write down what she says. You must imitate her manner of speech, of course, and find out from the play exactly how much she knows. You might allow the friend to get in a word occasionally, when Jane pauses to take breath.

47. Write a spell, in rhyme and in the style of "This

to That and That to This," which the Fairy might speak to undo what she has done.

48. Write a short story or a one-act play in which a boy or girl living in your town finds Aladdin's lamp in a lumber-room, and accidentally discovers its wonderful powers ; or a story or one-act play in which a fairy gives the boy or girl three wishes.

49. Draw and paint the peacock pie or Princess Myra's carriage.

BOOKS TO READ

50. *Alexander the Great* and *Archibald*, one-act plays by W. Graham Robertson. (In *The Slippers of Cinderella*, etc., with the author's illustrations.)

Peter Pan and Wendy, by J. M. Barrie.

Old King Cole, by Clifford Bax.

HERMON OULD : THE DISCOVERY

Mr. Hermon Ould, who has written a number of very interesting plays, has pictured vividly for us the moment of the discovery of America, the greatest discovery in the history of Europe. His " work of imagination " helps us to realize the truth of how that discovery was made.

You may be interested to know that the land which Columbus sighted was one of the Bahamas, probably Watling Island. He went ashore next morning to claim the island as Spanish territory, and was well received by the natives. Then, after visiting other islands, he sailed back to Spain to announce his discovery of the Indies—for he never knew that he had found a new continent.

ON TALKING IT OVER

51. The poop is the raised deck at the stern of the vessel. The quarter-deck is the part of the deck which

lies between the mainmast and the stern, including the poop; it is used by officers only. Why does Columbus go to the poop-head when he is looking for land?

52. What does Diego mean by saying, "We are like bats that fly by day"?

53. The variation of the compass, to which Pedro refers, occurred when the *Santa Maria* had sailed about six hundred miles to westward, and greatly alarmed the superstitious seamen.

54. What do you think of the answer which Francisco makes to Columbus: "There are limits to duty . . ."? (page 91).

55. Is the stage-direction, *He is paler than his wont, but very calm,* intended for the actor or the reader?

56. Why do the crew call Columbus an Italian renegade"?

57. In what way do all the similes resemble each other in Columbus's speech, ' Loyalty passes . . . at the first contact"? (page 94). Are they the kind of similes which you would expect him to use?

58. Why does he " peer more earnestly into the darkness"? (page 95).

59. It seems very easy for the mutinous seamen, 'thirty to one," to overpower Columbus and turn the ship homewards. Why do they not carry out their plan? (They did actually plan to throw him overboard.)

60. What does Columbus mean by " Your best cannot be bettered"? (page 95).

61. Why does he send Pepe away before he tells Pedro that he thought he saw a light?

62. Why does he give the order to heave to?

FOR PEN AND PENCIL

63. Imagine that you are Diego Garcia and write a short account of the attempted mutiny and the hailing of the light.

64. " Great men are meteors that consume themselves to light the earth."—Thomas Hardy. Mr. Ould prints this quotation on the title-page of *The Discovery.* How does it apply to Columbus? Do you know any other great men to whom it applies?

65. The character of Columbus has been described by those who knew him well. He was a brave man, not easily turned aside from anything which he had resolved to do. He had a strong imagination, and considerable faith in himself, he was generous, conscientious, and religious ; but he was not a good leader, because he could not handle men well, and being very quick-tempered and impulsive he often did things for which he was afterwards very sorry. His difficulties were due partly to these defects in his character, and partly to Spanish jealousy of him as a foreigner. (He was an Italian, born near Genoa : 1436 ?–1506.)

66. Show how far the play agrees with this description of his character : for example, try to find whether any of the things said and done by Columbus and said about him by others show that he was religious or not religious, brave or cowardly, and so on.

This is not very easy to do, but it is well worth trying. One can imagine Sherlock Holmes doing it with much interest. All the clues are in the play. What can you make of them ?

67. Write a dialogue in which an old sailor tells Columbus of the ancient tradition that the Vikings discovered land across the western ocean centuries before. (This tradition may have been one of the things which made Columbus resolve to set out on the voyage.)

68. Write a one-act play or short story from the following outline. Time: 1580. Scene: Deck of Francis Drake's ship, the *Golden Hind,* lying at anchor at Deptford. Drake has just returned from his three years' voyage round the world, with a shipload of treasure plundered from Spanish galleons and colonies. (Drake was the first Englishman to sail round the world.) Queen Elizabeth visits the ship with her courtiers and asks Drake many questions about his wonderful adventures. She is very pleased. As Spain and England are supposed to be at peace, the Spanish ambassador protests angrily against Drake's piracies, and expects Drake to be punished, for Spain is the richest and most powerful country in Europe, not to be lightly defied. Elizabeth replies by knighting Drake with the sword which she gave him when he left England. (Note that these details are partly imaginary.)

69. Find a picture of Columbus's ship, or of a small ship of his time, and copy it with pencil and water-colours.

70. Draw a map of the Atlantic Ocean, and show the track of Columbus's first voyage: Palos (August 3, 1492); Canary Islands (September 6); Bahama Islands (October 12); Cuba; Hayti; the mouth of the Tagus, near Lisbon (March 4, 1493); Palos (March 15).

BOOKS TO READ

71. *Joan the Maid* and *The Pathfinder*, one-act plays by Hermon Ould. (In *Plays of Pioneers.*)

BERNARD GILBERT: ELDORADO

Mr. Gilbert is playing a very fascinating game. Many writers have played it, and probably you have done so occasionally, but few people have been so thorough as Mr. Gilbert. Not content, like most of us, with creating an imaginary island or city in which we can wander and have adventures, he has invented "Bly District"—"a section of three or four hundred square miles, offered as an example of rural England, uncontaminated by English civilization. . . . Reference to the map shows it running up, from the sea, through successive belts of marsh, fen, sand, heath, moor, and limestone, embracing most kinds of soil and methods of cultivation, and nearly all classes of countryman." He has drawn the map of this country and written directories (like that at the head of this play) for every town and village. He knows all the people in his area, and is telling us about them in a succession of novels, plays, and poems.

ON TALKING IT OVER

72. For what purpose did the dramatist put in the opening dialogue between James and his son? (pages 102–104).

73. Why does Henry say, "This isn't fen-land"?

74. Why is James "scornful" when he says, "Of course not! That was after I told him I hadn't any to spare"?

75. Find three or four speeches in which James clearly shows his meanness.

76. Who is Tom Arch? (page 122).

77. Does the old man really get the better of Mrs. Burrows?

78. Which is the most enjoyable moment in the play?

FOR PEN AND PENCIL

79. You have seen only the bottom story of the old windmill as yet. Take a journey to the top story, and then write an account of all you have seen. (Remember Betsy's description, on pages 106–107).

80. Describe the fine view across Caxton Moor to Keal Hill.

81. Write a sequel to *Eldorado*, in the form of a dialogue or a one-act play, in which "Brother-in-law Japhet" learns from Mrs. Burrows what has happened to their potatoes. You have first of all to make up your mind as to what kind of people they are, how each will feel about the matter, and what Japhet is likely to do. You may bring in any characters from *Eldorado*.

82. Make a little rural comedy of your own, in two scenes, about the choir and the vicar in Mr. Thomas Hardy's story, *Under the Greenwood Tree* (Part II, chaps. ii. and iv.). You will have to cut down some of the longer speeches, and make a few additions and alterations. Remember that the story is copyright, which means that your play must not be performed in public without the author's permission, although you can do it as often as you like in the form-room or at home.

83. Draw a plan of an imaginary island or city of your

own, in which you would like to have adventures, and paint it in bright colours.

84. Write a short story or a one-act play about your adventures, keeping the plan in front of you as you write. You need not be your ordinary self, of course: you can be a pirate, or any one interesting.

BOOKS TO READ

85. *The Old Bull*, by Bernard Gilbert, in *Nine Modern Plays* (T.E.S.).

My First Book, by R. L. Stevenson. (It is in the T.E.S. edition of *Treasure Island*.)

There is another very interesting map at the beginning of *Prester John*, an excellent adventure story by John Buchan.

J. A. FERGUSON: CAMPBELL OF KILMOHR

If you live in the south of England you may think that this play is written in "bad English," but this is quite wrong. The characters speak Scots, which has been a distinct form of English for centuries and has a fine literature of its own, including the poems of Robert Burns and (in part at least) the novels of Sir Walter Scott. Now it is developing its own drama too, thanks largely to the Scottish National Players, of Glasgow, who act the best Scottish plays which they can find and act them well. Mr. Ferguson, who has written a number of novels and plays, has given us in *Campbell of Kilmohr* the finest Scottish tragedy, and Mr. John Brandane is now writing excellent comedies.

Campbell of Kilmohr is so good not only because it is cleverly written, but because it is so true to life, so simple and sincere. All the characters in it are real, living people, and the heroism of Mary and Dugald Stewart gives the play a fine nobility of feeling. It is worth reading many times, and well worth acting.

ON TALKING IT OVER

86. The " gift " is the gift of second-sight—of seeing things happening at a distance or in the future.

87. Who is the person to whom Stewart refers as " another and a greater " ?

88. What do you think happened when Stewart ran into the sentry " round the bend beyond Kilrain " ?

89. Why does Morag push the dirk away and hide her face in her hands ?

90. Why did Pharaoh spare the butler ?

91. You will find the story of Haman, and how he came to be hanged on a gallows seventy feet high, in the Old Testament : *Esther*, chaps. iii.–vii.

92. If you do not know the meaning of " proscription " and " contumacy," look them up in a dictionary. The " capital charge " here means punishment by death.

93. Does Campbell really obtain the information which he requires ?

94. When do you most dislike Campbell ?

95. There is one sentence on page 142 which might very well be taken as a motto for the whole play ; and there is another on page 144. Can you find them both ?

96. Is Mary Stewart sad because her son is dead ?

97. In what way does Dugald Stewart resemble Christopher Columbus ?

98. How does this play differ from all the other plays in this book ?

FOR PEN AND PENCIL

99. If you turn back to the paragraph about Columbus's character, No. 65, you will see that it tells you his chief characteristics and then asks you to find things in the play which show these characteristics. Now, do the opposite with Campbell. Read through the play very carefully, making notes about the things which he says and does, and which are said about him. For example, if he says or does something which shows that he is a coward, then make a note of it. When you have been through the whole play in this way, arrange your notes

carefully, and then write a description of Campbell's character.

100. Write a short account of any one who has given his life heroically for a cause in which he believed. If you do not know of any one, you should read Sir Arthur Quiller-Couch's fine book called *The Roll Call of Honour* (T.E.S.).

101. This play is tragic, but not sad. Can you explain why it is not?

102. Write a paragraph in praise of Dugald Stewart, or Mary Stewart.

BOOKS TO READ

103. *The Escape of Prince Charles Edward*, in *A Book of Escapes and Hurried Journeys*, by John Buchan (T.E.S.).

The Secret of the Heather Ale, by Neil Munro, in *Modern Short Stories* (T.E.S.). A story of a desperate battle between two Highland clans.

Midwinter, by John Buchan (T.E.S.). A tale of the '45 Rebellion.

MAURICE BARING: CATHERINE PARR

Probably you have not read or seen a play like this before. It is one of a number of *Diminutive Dramas* in which the Honourable Maurice Baring makes good-humoured fun of many people who are famous in history and legend—Jason, Odysseus, Julius Cæsar, Alfred the Great, and others. The author has treated history much as Mr. Milne has treated fairy tales, and with the same enjoyable results. This is a very good play to act, and easy to stage.

ON TALKING IT OVER

104. "A woman of your experience" is Henry's unpleasant reminder that Catherine was a widow when he married her. She retorts by reminding him—of what?

105. Henry was a good musician. He played several instruments, sang well, and composed a number of songs. What is assonance ?

106. His pride in his music was equalled by his pride in his learning, which he shows here by referring to the Greek writers, Plutarch, Xenophon, and Aristotle.

107. Bucephalus is pronounced Bū-sĕf′-a-lŭs.

The pronunciation of the Greek which Henry quotes cannot be well represented in English letters, so if you can find no one to tell you exactly how to say it, you had better leave it out when acting the play.

108. " My family has no blood on its escutcheon." Henry had executed two of his wives and many of his enemies. What does " escutcheon " mean, and what does it stand for here ?

109. Dr. Butts, afterwards Sir William Butts, was the King's physician. His reply by the page, " Dr. Butts says your Majesty was quite correct as to the colour of Alexander the Great's horse," is one of the best things in the play. What is the point of it ? What does it tell you about Dr. Butts ?

110. When is Henry (*a*) most on his dignity, (*b*) most angry, (*c*) most good-tempered, (*d*) most anxious to please his wife ?

111. Which is Catherine's most spiteful remark ?

112. At what point are they quarrelling most furiously?

113. Do you like the people in this play ?

114. Like *The Discovery*, this is a play about people who actually lived in the past, but it is very different. What are the chief differences ? Would you call it a historical play ?

FOR PEN AND PENCIL

115. The dramatist has not given many stage-directions. Copy out the passage from " I suppose you mean I am a bigot " to " a great many letters to write," adding full stage-directions. You may begin like this :

King Henry [*his temper rising again*]. I suppose you mean I am a bigot ?

Catherine [*indignantly*]. You can turn what one says into meaning anything you like. [*Injured and emphatic*]

As a matter of fact, all I said was that the horse was black.

116. Write two short letters from Henry and Catherine respectively, in which they describe the quarrel to friends of theirs. You may be sure that they have very different ideas of what happened, and that each is convinced that the other was altogether in the wrong. Show this as clearly and humorously as you can.

117. Write a one-act play about any historical characters, in the same style as this play. If you choose the incident of King Alfred and the Cakes you may be able to compare your play with the one in *Diminutive Dramas* on the same subject.

118. Find a picture of Henry VIII., and copy it carefully. The best is the famous portrait by Hans Holbein, a great painter of his time. The picture on page 146 is copied from this portrait, but gives only the head and shoulders.

119. Draw a plan of the stage, showing the positions of the table, chairs, bookcase, and entrances, and of the characters when Henry is telling the Page to find the Chamberlain.

BOOKS TO READ

120. *Diminutive Dramas*, by Maurice Baring. Numbers 5, 7, and 18. One of the best of these, *The Rehearsal*, is in *Nine Modern Plays* (T.E.S.).

Shakespeare's *Henry VIII.*, or *The Queen and the Cardinal*, in Evelyn Smith's *Little Plays from Shakespeare, Second Series* (T.E.S.).

MILES MALLESON: MICHAEL

Mr. Malleson has made this play from a story by Count Leo Tolstoy (1828–1910), the great Russian novelist, dramatist, thinker, and social reformer. "What Men Live By" is a story with a moral, like so many of Tolstoy's writings, for he gave much thought to the great problem of how men should live so as to make the very best of life, for their fellow-men and for themselves. And he wrote often of the Russian peasants, whom he knew and loved well, even before he gave away all his possessions so that he himself could live the simple life of a peasant. The glimpses of that life which we have in *Michael* are as true as they are vivid.

ON TALKING IT OVER

121. " You must be a bad man—[because] you are afraid," says Matryona. Do you agree with her reasoning ?

122. What do you feel about Michael after Aniuska's behaviour towards him at the end of Scene I. ?

123. What do you think of the nobleman ? What do you learn from the way in which Simon takes orders from him ?

124. When the news comes that the nobleman is dead, what do you think of Michael ?

125. Choose two adjectives to describe the character of each of the following : Simon, Matryona, The Woman.

126. If *Michael* were written in one scene instead of three, how would it be arranged ? Do you think it would be as good ?

127. What would be the chief problem in performing the play, and how would you solve it ?

128. Which is the most striking incident in the play, and which the most impressive moment ?

129. Do you know any sentence in the New Testament which might be taken as a motto for the whole play ?

FOR PEN AND PENCIL

130. Write down a title for each of the three scenes.

131. Explain how the three incidents taught Michael the three great truths which he had to learn.

132. Imagine that you are Simon *or* Matryona, and write a short account of the happenings in the last scene.

133. Say what you have learned from the play about Russian peasant-life.

134. Re-read the stage direction at the head of Scene I., and then draw a picture of the interior of Simon's hut.

BOOKS TO READ

135. *What Men live by, Iván the Fool, The Bear-hunt,* and *Two Old Men,* in *Twenty-three Tales by Tolstoy,* translated by L. and A. Maude. Oxford Press.

Paddly Pools and *The Little White Thought,* one-act plays by Miles Malleson. Henderson.

Brother Wolf and *Sister Gold,* one-act plays by Laurence Housman. Sidgwick and Jackson.

GENERAL

136. Which of the plays in this book do you like most, and which do you like least ? Give your reasons.

137. Describe any amusing incident in the plays.

138. Which character in the plays do you most admire, and why ?

139. Arrange the plays under the following headings : Comedies, Tragedies, Historical Plays, "Moralities."

140. Draw and paint and cut out scenery for any one of the plays, and set it up as it would be on the stage.

141. Draw a stage plan for *The Slippers of Cinderella,* or Scene II. of *Robin Hood,* then choose an exciting moment in the play and show on the plan where you think that the characters would be standing at that moment.

142. Which plays in this book would you choose as most suitable for performance (1) at your school speech-day, (2) at a school concert, given at the end of the Christmas term, (3) by a Scout Troop, (4) by an O. T. C., and (5) by a branch of the League of Nations Union ? Explain the reasons for your choice in each case.

143. Draw up from this book a programme of two, three, or four plays (according to the number of actors available) for performance by your own form or society. Choose and arrange the plays very carefully, to make a good and varied programme. Then cast the plays (that is, choose the actors), giving every person available the part for which he or she is most suited, omitting no one, and in a very few cases giving two parts to one player if this proves necessary. A play which cannot be cast fairly well should not be put in the programme.

144. When you have drawn up this programme of plays, write a short prologue for it, in rhymed verse.

145. Which part would you choose for yourself in your programme, and why?

146. Make a model theatre, with a painted stage-setting for any play in this book, figures of the characters painted and cut out, and electric lighting from "pea-bulbs," and a pocket-lamp battery, if you wish. You can give a performance of the play, preferably with one or two people to help you read the parts "behind the scenes." Full instructions for all this are to be found in *Everybody's Theatre*, written and illustrated by H. W. Whanslaw. (Wells Gardner, Darton, and Co., 5s.)

A SUGGESTION FOR FORM-ROOM ACTING

147. Elect leaders from the form and make each of them responsible for one of the plays which you wish to act. Having decided how many players are needed for each play, the leaders, taking turns, choose their companies from the form, and then each company prepares a "performance" of its play, to be given with the rest of the form as audience. The leader should act as "producer" in the preliminary rehearsal or rehearsals, and assign parts and positions on the "stage" and suggest movements, etc.

The performances can be very simple, with all the actors reading their parts, or they can be more elaborate, with some or all of the parts learned by heart and costumes improvised or borrowed. In any case simple properties and stage furniture are a great help. Plays acted in this way can be very enjoyable, and there is the advantage that if rehearsals can be held in a large room or in the open air, all the plays can be rehearsed at the same time.

ON WRITING LITTLE PLAYS

148. Having enjoyed the plays in this book, you may like to try your hand as a playwright. To write good plays demands ability of a special kind, and a first-hand knowledge of stage conditions, so you need not be surprised if you do not produce a masterpiece; but the attempt is well worth making, and can be very good fun. You may prefer to begin work on your play without more ado, following your own methods, but if you would like to write a play good enough for performance by your own form or school society, you may find a few hints useful.

149. First of all, for the plot. If you can invent this yourself, so much the better. Perhaps you can write about a historical character in whom you are interested, or an incident in the history of your own town or village or school. Several of these incidents, dramatized by yourself and your friends after you have talked things over, could be put together to make a little pageant, or a " chronicle play " about the life of a great man or woman of the past.

150. If you do not invent your own play, you can follow one of the suggestions already made in this book, or else take an incident from a story and make it into a play, as Mr. Malleson has done with *Michael*. There are many such incidents to be found in novels by Dickens, Sir Walter Scott, R. L. Stevenson, Rudyard Kipling, Sir Arthur Conan Doyle, and other writers. Perhaps your teacher will suggest some incidents from books which are in your school or form library.* A number of books in the " Teaching of English Series " are specially useful. *Pattern Plays*, by E. C. Oakden and Mary Sturt, contains stories, plays made from these stories, and further stories to be made into plays, with hints as to how it should be

* Copyright work must not be used in public without special permission from the owner of the copyright.

done. John Buchan's *A Book of Escapes* and *The Path of the King* are treasure-houses of short, exciting incidents, and the non-copyright books include *The Arabian Nights*, Kingsley's *The Heroes*. *Scenes from "Quentin Durward,"* and the stories in Sir Henry Newbolt's *The Greenwood*. Whether you invent your plot or borrow it, you will find it a good plan to write it down briefly before you begin on the play. It is much better to have your play in one fairly long scene (or act) than in several short scenes, so try to arrange it like this if you can. For instance, *The Slippers of Cinderella* would not be nearly so good, and would be much harder to stage, if it were written in several scenes—one in which the Tremaines learn that they have lost all their money, and another in which they move into the small house in which we see them, and so on.

151. Then make up your mind who the people are, and what they are like, and try to make them different from each other. Notice how different Campbell is from Dugald Stewart, and Columbus from Guillermo Ires, and Myra from Agatha. They behave differently, and have different ways of talking about the same thing.

152. The first thing the characters have to do is to let the audience know who they are, and which are friends and which are enemies, and anything important which has been happening. If you re-read the beginning of *The Slippers of Cinderella* and *Michael* you will see how cleverly the dramatist makes his characters tell the audience all about themselves, by talking to each other. One method is to make a character who has been away ask another to explain what has happened during his absence. But do not have too much explaining.

153. Then "the plot thickens" until the play reaches its climax, which is the most exciting part, the highest point, so to speak. Try to find the climax of *Robin Hood*, Scene II., *Campbell of Kilmohr*, *The Discovery*, and *Michael*.

154. After the climax the plot is unravelled, the questions which the audience have been asking about the characters are answered, and the play comes to an end. You can learn a great deal by studying the plays in this volume, and by comparing *Michael* with the short story from which it is made.

155. Finally, before you start writing, turn to the beginning of one of the plays and see how it is arranged. Write the title, your name as author, a list of characters, and a short description of the scenery, and then begin the dialogue. Notice where the printer has put capitals, full stops, brackets, and italics, and copy this arrangement. You can't put words in italics when you are writing, so you underline them instead. Take a fresh line for each speech, and write as neatly as you can. It is a good plan to write first on loose sheets of paper, and on one side only, so that alterations can be made easily, and then to copy your work into a book—again leaving alternate pages blank. You will find much more on the subject of play-writing in *Nine Modern Plays.*

SOME BOOKS ON MODERN DRAMA

(Not intended for junior readers)

A Study of the Modern Drama. Barrett H. Clark. Appleton and Co.

This valuable book, an encyclopædia of facts and critical ideas, is particularly suitable for the school library and for reading circles, because it suggests lines of thought rather than offers definite conclusions. Half the book is given to English, Irish, and American drama ; the other half to the drama of Norway, Russia, France, and other European countries. Exceptionally useful bibliographies and index.

Modern Drama. J. W. Marriott. The " Little Theatre " Series. Nelson.

An illuminating survey of drama in England, Europe, and America, from the late nineteenth century to the present year. A guide to all the most interesting modern plays and playwrights. Fully indexed.

Drama. Ashley Dukes. Home University Library,

A very interesting essay, of unusual scope. Chapters on the Nature and Varieties of Drama, The Dramatist, The Actor, The Producer, The Scene, The Playhouse,

The Audience, and Drama Present and Future. Bibliography.

On the Art of the Theatre. Edward Gordon Craig. Heinemann.

One of the most stimulating, provocative, and original books ever written on the arts of stage production.

The English Theatre. Allardyce Nicoll. Illustrated. Nelson.

From Roman times to 1936—the only complete history, by the writer whom the *Times* has recently described as " the foremost historian of the British theatre." With a complete annotated list of London theatres, past and present, bibliography, and index.

ACTING NOTES

These brief notes on the plays in this collection are intended for those who know little or nothing of the art of dramatic production. There are several excellent books for the amateur, which teach as much as it is possible to teach of any art in a book, and it is not proposed to attempt to write a complete guide in this limited space, but to attempt instead what none of the books give—a detailed account of the production of a particular play, *The Discovery*. The notes on the other plays, suggestive, not exhaustive, will be merely supplementary to this account.

THE DISCOVERY

We will assume that this play has been chosen because it can be cast fairly well from the actors available, offers a fairly large number of parts (for a one-act play), is not difficult or expensive to dress and stage, and—most important of all—it is worth doing. (For some societies it will have the further attraction that all the characters are men, though one can imagine it performed quite well by a company of girls.)

The Producer.—When the society has organized its activities and finances (see the books recommended on page 226), the producer must set to work.

The producer is to the play what the conductor is to the orchestra. He is responsible for the artistic harmony and unity of the play in all its details. He must have the power of final decision in all matters affecting this artistic harmony, and upon his tact and energy and enthusiasm, his knowledge and imagination, his willingness to experiment and learn, the success of the play will depend to a very large extent.

Casting is the first problem, whether it is done by a small committee or by the producer alone. In the case of untried actors, the best plan is to begin with "auditions" or trial readings, at which the candidates for parts can read in turn various characters in *The Discovery*. The casting authority can then decide from voice, manner, and apparent acting potentialities, how the play is to be cast. Columbus is most important of course, and the actor who is to take this part should have a good presence and ability to assume the dignity and habit of command which are required. Don Pedro is a gentleman also, but of less striking personality. The remaining characters, except the boy Pepe, should be much less cultured in voice and manner.

If the players are juniors, convincing and realistic characterization is obviously not to be expected, but the casting should be done as carefully as with adult players.

Understudies are a valuable insurance against disaster, and some societies choose two casts, which work quite independently of each other, and are responsible for alternate performances.

Permission to perform the play should now be secured, and this must always be done before rehearsals begin, because occasionally a play is not available for amateurs. For *The Discovery*, application must be made to the author's agents, Messrs. Samuel French, 26 Southampton Street, Strand, London, W.C.2, without whose written permission no performance may be given. The royalty for each performance is 10s. 6d., payable in advance. (The play takes about forty minutes.) The society is bound in honour to pay the royalty, which is in many cases the chief source of the dramatist's income, and is simply a payment for the right to use his property. A dramatist should never be asked to waive his royalty because the performance is in aid of charity, for he prefers to choose for himself the charities to which he is to contribute. (Such performances are good for charity and bad for amateur drama ; they suggest that the latter is not on its own account worth paying to see.) An increasing number of dramatists, however, accept percentage royalties instead of fixed fees, on which point inquiries may be made of the British Drama League.

Business arrangements, such as booking a hall, advertising the play, and distributing tickets, should be made well in advance. *The Discovery* will obviously not make a complete programme by itself. Schools and some other educational institutions may get exemption from the entertainment tax by application on the Form E.D.23, which can be obtained from the local Customs and Excise Office.

The Stage.—There is a great deal to be said for the stage simply set with screens or hung with curtains (see the books by Mr. Barrett Clark and Mr. Harold Ridge). At least for those amateurs with no stage of their own, scenery is usually an expense and trouble out of all proportion to its worth, and most amateur scenery is artistically inferior to curtains. *The Discovery* may be played if necessary on a stage draped round with black or dark blue curtains, and bare of properties ; the audience will not resent this simplicity if the acting is good. The great advantage of a simple setting is that it concentrates attention upon the actors and leaves a clearer picture of the play in the mind of the spectator, and the shorter the play the greater is the gain.* For *The Discovery* the setting shown in the stage-plan on p. 205 is suggested as a suitable combination of simplicity and of appeal to the imagination of the audience. It should be possible to most small societies, but if the raised platform for the poop cannot be contrived, the directions for stage movements which are given below can still be used without alteration.

The surround, shown by the wavy line, consists of curtains of black velveteen (or cheaper material), or dark blue serge ; with good lighting they will suggest the night sky excellently. The bulwarks, about four feet high—or less if the actors are short—consists of canvas stretched on wooden frames or, failing this, of a row of butter boxes ; † either can be distempered or painted, to repre-

* Mr. Percival Wilde tells the story of a twenty-minutes play of his which was so successful when acted by amateurs on a curtained stage, with very simple dresses and properties, that it was taken up by a millionaire theatre magnate. He spent large sums in giving the play the sumptuous dresses and architectural setting which he thought it needed, and then found that it was a complete failure ; by the time the audience had done looking at the dresses and scenery, and begun to attend to the dialogue, the play was over !

† These boxes are cheap, strong, and very useful to a small society, for they can be distempered any colour and used for many purposes—to make battlements, for instance, or a dais, or the table in *Robin Hood.*

sent the wooden ribs and panels of the ship's side. (Columbus's vessel was a square-rigged, three-masted ship of 230 tons, 95 feet long, and $25\frac{1}{2}$ feet wide, with high poop and forecastle, rounded bow and square stern. There is a good picture in *A History of Everyday Things in England,* vol. i., page 155.) If space is limited the raised platform constituting the poop need not occupy much of the stage, since little action takes place on it. In this case the top of the poop is not seen, and the large lantern may be transferred to the place indicated in the plan. It is not at all difficult to make a beautiful lantern. On a small stage the poop cannot be high, but eighteen inches is suggested as a minimum. This gives a flight of three steps, each of them nine to twelve inches deep. (Sets of steps, and of small platforms to stand on trestles, are most useful, for they will serve for many plays in a variety of combinations and positions. Only the producer who has worked with them knows what a boon it is to be able to develop the action of a play in three dimensions instead of two.) There should be a rail along the edge of the poop and down both sides of the steps, low enough and open enough not to obscure the players at all. The top of this rail and of the bulwarks may be picked out with a line of white paint if they are not clear enough in the dim light. The masts, which are not essential, are made of cylinders of canvas or casement cloth, sewn firmly to rings at top and bottom and then drawn taut ; or of tile-battens, nailed at top and bottom, two or three inches apart, around three-quarters of the circumference of two wooden discs, this cylindrical cage being covered with material. To these may be added if desired a few thick ropes (shrouds), drawn tight so that they appear to stretch from the bulwarks to the maintop ; and a strip of light-coloured material, to represent the lower edge of a sail, curving over the actors' heads, at right angles to the bulwarks. The sail has no lower yard. From the foot of the poop to the mainmast is the quarter-deck. The waist, foremast, and forecastle are off stage to the right.

Lighting for this play is important, but simple. There should be an electric bulb or group of bulbs fixed inside the proscenium, right or right centre, and so shrouded by setting them in boxes or tin funnels that their light falls

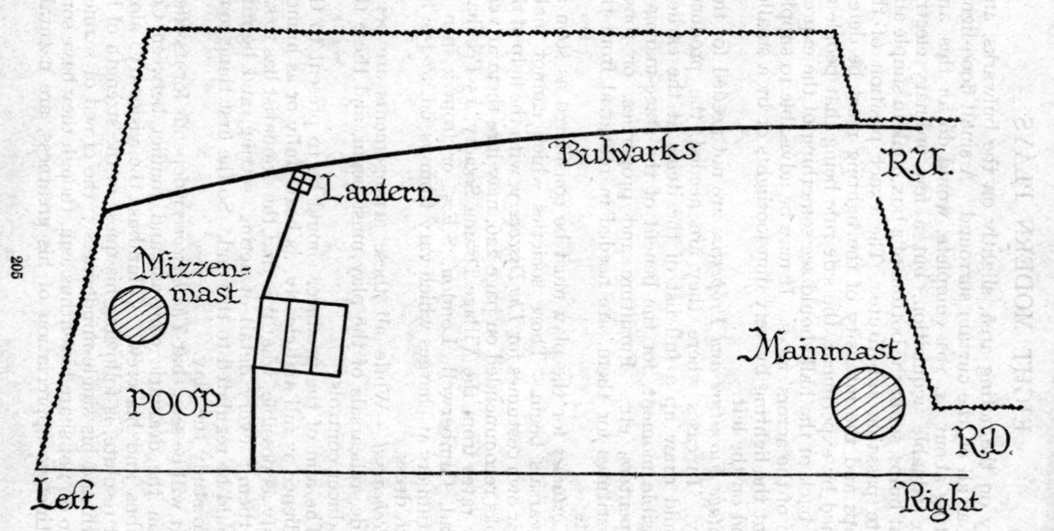
Bulwarks
R.U.
Lantern
Mizzen-mast
Mainmast
POOP
R.D.
Left
Right

fully on the acting area, slightly on the bulwarks, and not at all on the curtain surround. A small flood-light, costing about £4, 10s. complete, would do for this, and is a valuable acquisition, but a few ordinary electric light bulbs, set in the bottom of a box, make a simple and quite passable substitute. The exact position of the lamps and the intensity of the lighting must be determined by experiment, the safe rule being that people at the back of the hall should see something of the expression of the actors' faces. It may be advisable to supplement the lighting by very dim footlights or by a smaller flood on the left.

Stage Furniture and Properties are not needed for this play. In cases where they are needed, the producer should draw up a full list of the items at the earliest possible moment, for the benefit of the stage-manager, carpenters, etc. Furniture and properties, or rough substitutes for them, are needed in rehearsal from the first.

Costumes for the play must be considered as soon as rehearsals begin. Those societies which cannot make their own costumes for *The Discovery*, with the help of the books recommended on page 226, may hire them at very low rates from the Village Drama Society, 15 Peckham Road, Camberwell, London, S.E.5, or from a firm of costumiers at charges which vary from 7s. 6d. to 25s. for each dress.

Rehearsal.—While all these arrangements are being made, rehearsals of the play must begin, and these the producer controls.

The aim of the producer should be to present to the audience as full and clearly, as beautifully or as humorously as possible, what it is that the dramatist has to say to them; every detail of acting, setting, and lighting should be regulated to this end. So the first thing to do is to study the play.

It will be seen that *The Discovery* depends for its effect upon the dramatic contrast and conflict between Columbus and his crew. Columbus, the visionary, alone but resolute, is following his quest in the strength of his faith and his single-mindedness; the crowd of seamen, who do not share his enthusiasm, though they have some instinctive appreciation of his greatness, are naturally most concerned for their own safety. Though they have the advantage of numbers and the spur of superstitious fear, they are uncertain of themselves and their aims, and lack a good leader, so that Columbus is able to keep them at bay until the sight of land saves the situation. (In all this the play is fairly true to history.) Don Pedro stands between the admiral and the crew, doubting Columbus, but ashamed to oppose him.

The play therefore has to be "worked" to bring out these ideas, and however young the players may be, the performance (and the players) will gain greatly if the producer has a clear conception of the theme of the play.

The stage directions given in the text are inadequate for production, so they must be supplemented. Some producers decide every detail of movement, grouping, and gesture, with a model stage and puppets, before they begin rehearsing; others decide only the main outlines, and fill in the details with the actors. The producer must work out his own artistic salvation in this as in many other matters, but at least he must go to the first rehearsal with the entrances and exits and important stage movements clear in his mind and on his scrip. A stage-plan is necessary, and smaller plans showing the positions of the characters at important points in the action are a great help. For *The Discovery* we may decide as follows:

When the curtain rises, Diego and Juan are both down stage * to the extreme right, in front of the mast. Diego is standing, facing towards the right, and holding with his left hand a rope which comes down to the deck at his feet from a point above his head and out of sight. Juan, facing left, is kneeling at Diego's feet and fastening the rope to a bolt at the foot of the mast. It should be made as plain as possible that they are not interested in what they are doing, but in what they are saying to each other. Their voices must be low, but with good enunciation they will be clearly heard if, after the curtain rises, they wait a moment until the rustling of the audience subsides.

To emphasize the "*gracious* madman" Juan sits back on his heels. The song of the seamen is heard from the

* "Down stage" means towards the audience, and "up stage" away from the audience, a reminder that stages used to be built sloping up towards the back.

wings to the right; Juan stands up and turns facing front and looking off right when he says, "They ought to stop that." At Diego's "'Sh!" both kneel and fumble with the rope.

Pedro enters up stage right, going towards the poop steps, and stops short at right centre when he sees the two seamen. Diego stands up and turns to face Pedro at the latter's "Who's that?" "And an uglier deed" is the cue for Juan to rise, salute, and go off, down stage, right, and for Columbus to enter, up stage, right. He is going towards the poop steps, and he too stops short, with a quick suspicious glance, when he sees the two men talking. He is down stage centre. Pedro draws back up stage a step, so that Columbus can speak to Diego. When Columbus "*points off*" Diego makes a movement to confront him in open defiance, hesitates, weakens, and turns away to go off, slowly and with obvious reluctance, down stage right. Columbus looks after him for a second before speaking. When the two have gone on to the poop, Pepe can enter down stage, right, and remain behind the mainmast, in full sight of the audience, but hidden from Columbus and Pedro. (A hatchway is likely to be difficult and is in no way essential.) On the poop Columbus is well down stage, left, looking out over the audience, and Pedro is a pace behind him. He turns on Pedro at "You, too." They are both rigidly attentive during the song, and then as he says, "*Madre de Dios*, they drink too much," Columbus strides purposefully down to the quarter-deck as though he were going to forbid the singing, but pauses centre, and turns, at the words of Pedro, who has followed him more slowly. Both remain centre until Pedro, crossing in front of Columbus, goes off up stage, right. Columbus then paces slowly and thoughtfully to the extreme left of the quarter-deck below the steps, speaking as he goes. He turns abruptly towards Pepe when the latter leaves his place by the mainmast and runs up the steps, to come down again immediately and approach Columbus, who stands his ground. Pedro comes to the centre, up stage a little, and Pepe, when told to go, passes behind Pedro and stands by the bulwarks, up stage right centre. Columbus takes a step towards the right when he cries, "Hallo, there!" and Francisco, entering from the right, down stage, comes to the centre when he says, " Our power of endurance has gone," and Columbus goes to him at " Francisco, let me plead with you." Both look to the right, Francisco half-turning, when " *the song swells up again.*" Columbus's command, " Boy, come here," brings Pepe down stage to him, Francisco stepping back to the right and a little up stage. Columbus turns his back to the audience when he tells Pedro, who is standing at the head of the poop steps, to have Guillermo sent. When the angry seamen crowd on to the quarter-deck from both entrances, right, Pedro pauses half-way down the poop steps, Columbus stands fast, and Francisco draws back up stage to join the other seamen. All these must have their exact positions assigned to them (or they may stand in a straight line) with Guillermo and Diego in the forefront, on either side of the mast, the former up stage of the latter. Guillermo comes down stage to right centre when he " *advances towards Columbus*," who takes a step forward at " Don Guillermo." Guillermo draws back doubtfully to his former position by the mast at " Now return to your duties," and a moment later Diego starts forward. When Columbus has mounted the poop he turns left and stands a little down stage of the head of the steps, Pedro being on the other side of them. The men crowd forward to centre at " Have him down ! " and when Pepe, " after intervening," goes up the steps, they draw back a little. When Columbus " *looks out at sea* " he looks over the audience, standing rigidly and peering, and evidently forgetting the seamen entirely until their movement recalls his attention. Guillermo " *slinks off* " down stage, right. Francisco speaks from centre, and then follows Guillermo. The others go out slowly and hesitatingly, up stage or down, and Pepe follows them a moment later. Then the wild shout of " Land ! " breaks in with startling suddenness upon the intense but restrained excitement of Pedro and Columbus.

At the first rehearsal the only thing for the actors to do is to " read for position "—reading their parts without expression, and simply learning their movements. After this the actors should make themselves word perfect in their parts as quickly as they can : it is a mistake for actors, especially if they are young and inexperienced, to be set to learn their parts before rehearsals begin.

The play then has to be built up at successive rehearsals—twenty or more may be necessary—and when it is in mechanically good "going order" at the right speeds (amateurs are notorious for speaking too slowly or too quickly, without variation of pace), the producer can work for "atmosphere," for all those little subtleties of intonation and movement which make the supreme difference between a living work of art and a mechanical performance.

The actors, as well as the producer, will have much to learn, and the latter should be prepared to give training in speech and movement if it is needed. Every word of the play must be audible to people in the back row of the audience, and this is a question not of shouting, but of correct pitch and clear enunciation. Speech normally should be as pleasant and natural as possible, without any "elocution for elocution's sake."

Actors must speak to the front when they can reasonably do so; not pass in front of any one who is speaking or distract attention from him; stand still, when they do stand still, without being stiff and without shuffling about; and move definitely when they do move. All movements must be natural or made to appear natural, not merely obvious devices for "changing the picture."

The producer should do everything he can to encourage players to "think themselves into" their parts,* to understand as fully as they can what they are doing and saying and feeling, and *to act all the time they are on the stage*, not merely while they are speaking. And they must learn to take their cues very promptly, so that there are no little gaps in between speeches. Every actor should understand the entire play, and regard its success as a whole as a much more important thing than his individual success in his own part; though he must

* "Unfortunately it is superficially easier to teach by the imitative method than by any other. It is much simpler to say "Copy me" than it is to arouse a sluggish mind to think continually and vividly, or to awaken in minds which are purely intellectual an emotional response. To train and develop the great imaginative faculty of the mind, to balance the emotional response by intellectual thought, and to induce the student to bring his voice, face, and body under his own mental control, requires much more time, patience, and ability from the teacher than exhibiting himself as an example."—LOUIE BAGLEY.

realize that his own part, however small, is vital to the whole.

Make-up.—This fascinating art is dealt with in the books recommended on page 226. The dim lighting of this play may not demand complete make-up (covering the whole face, neck, and ears), in which case a little colour in the cheeks and darkening of the brows will be all the grease-paint needed : but this must be determined by experiment. All the characters except Pepe should wear beards and moustaches, those of the seamen being unkempt. As the appearance of Columbus is not familiar there is no necessity to attempt to reproduce it, but the following description of him, which has been left by his friend and companion, Las Casas, may be of interest: "He had a figure that was above medium height, a countenance long and imposing, an aquiline nose, clear blue eyes, a light complexion tinged with red, beard and hair blonde in youth, but early turned to white." There are several portraits of him in existence, but none that is certainly authentic.

The Dress Rehearsal should be a day or two days before the performance, and should be as much like a performance as possible, with full lighting, stage setting, dresses, and make-up, and a small select audience if desired. The producer should let it go through without interruption or alteration if these can possibly be avoided; but he may give a few words of final advice to the cast—emphasizing especially that they must keep the play going whatever happens in performance : it is astonishing what audiences will not notice, if the players do not hesitate. If they are to take a "final curtain" this should be rehearsed, or it will almost certainly be muddled.

There is no need for any one to worry if the dress rehearsal is altogether miserable and depressing. Dress rehearsals often are ; but if the play has been faithfully rehearsed it will spring into full life in the performance.

The Programme should give the names of the actors in the order in which they appear or speak. This avoids any question as to precedence, and is an aid to the audience in identifying characters.

The Performance.—The producer's responsibility ends, in theory, with the dress rehearsal, when it passes to the stage manager, who is responsible for the stage setting, furniture, properties, and so on. But the producer will be well advised to remain in the wings to deal with any emergency and help keep the cast in good spirits. They may be comforted with the information that many experienced professional actors are always nervous before they go on !

The chief essentials for an artistic production are good team work, imagination, enthusiasm, loyalty, and an infinite capacity for taking pains. It will be noticed that wealth is not included. One of the most delightful things about amateur dramatic work is the fine results which may be obtained with slender means.

THE PRINCESS AND THE WOODCUTTER

The fee for each and every representation of this play by amateurs is one guinea, payable in advance to Messrs. Samuel French, Ltd., 26 Southampton Street, Strand, W.C.2, or their authorized representatives. No public performance may be given unless this written permission has first been obtained.

The time of acting is about thirty minutes.

The Princess and the Woodcutter is make-believe, and if it is played quickly and lightly, with enjoyment and without hitches, all will be well. If it drags slowly along with careful realism it will probably be very dull indeed. The audience is not asked to take it seriously at all, but only to be amused at the dramatist's lightness and deftness of touch, and the unexpected turns which he gives to a familiar situation. A bright Third or Fourth Form, with that quality of eager alertness which marks young actors of promise, could make the play very amusing, if it were thoroughly rehearsed to secure the lightness and smoothness of movement which are essential.

Staging could hardly be simpler—green curtains, or better still a real glade or a garden, with a bench and a few logs for the woodcutter to chop. Dresses could very well be copied from Heath Robinson's illustrations to Hans Andersen, or the pictures in *Shakespeare for Community Players* or *The Bankside Costume Book*. Both King and Queen should have large crowns, and if they look as though their wearers sleep in them, so much the better. Music for the songs is obtainable from Messrs. Samuel French, but if necessary they can easily be omitted, and so of course can the revels.

ROBIN HOOD

For permission to perform this play application must be made to Messrs. A. P. Watt & Sons, Hastings House, Norfolk Street, Strand, London, W.C.2, and no performance may be given until permission has been obtained. The royalty payable varies with the circumstances.

The play takes about fifteen minutes.

Whether this play is to be acted on the edge of a shrubbery or a wood, or on a stage indoors, it presents little difficulty in staging. Both the gallows and the silver birch at which Marian shoots must be off stage, so that Robin and Marian fire into the wings—which, in the open air, can be simply clumps of bushes or trees. Similarly, both the hut and the cave can be off stage if desired. The oak to which Robin Hood sets his back may be changed into any other tree for open-air performance, or if the play is being given indoors the tree may be dispensed with altogether by omitting Prince John's reference to it. It is easy to dispense with the Knight's horse. For the table a low box or bench or table, completely covered by green turfs or a green material such as serge, will serve very well. If good bows and arrows cannot be borrowed locally, boys will find great pleasure in making them, and should be encouraged to search any available books for information.

For indoor performances a stage draped with green curtains, and set with shrubs (not formal ones) in pots, will be quite adequate.

An open-air performance is likely to be better, and easier to arrange, and the lack of a front curtain presents a problem only at the end of Scene II. It might be solved by the party settling down to their meal after Shadow-of-a-Leaf's concluding speech, while one of the outlaws sings a song : when the song is finished they can all troop away. At the beginning of Scene I. the rustics and townsfolk enter from one direction : at the end the

Knight and outlaws hurry after Robin Hood, and the crowd follows the Sheriff. Then the stage is left empty for a few moments, and the change of scene is sufficiently indicated by Marian's opening speech, as she and the others enter, evidently in great anxiety.

Full instructions for making all the dresses required for the play are to be found in *The Bankside Costume Book* (see page 227), and only the Knight's armour presents any difficulty. The outlaws' dress is particularly simple and graceful: tunics, shorts, and stockings of Lincoln green; socks with their tops rolled down almost to the ankles, for boots; felt hats or close-fitting caps decked with feathers. Belts, daggers, etc., can be of bright contrasting colours.

The play is very suitable for young players, for it is so direct and simple; the keynote is struck by the excellent stage direction, *Enter Robin Hood, disguised as an old beggar, with a green patch on one eye.* There are no subtleties of characterization: Robin Hood is a hero and Prince John is a villain, without qualification. Young actors, believing unreservedly in the play, may well give a more interesting performance than adults. The essentials are speed and vigour, and the fighting, the shooting, and the movements and murmurs of the crowd must not be left to the inspiration of the moment: they must be rehearsed exactly and thoroughly.

THE SLIPPERS OF CINDERELLA

The fee for each representation of this play by amateurs is seven shillings and sixpence, payable in advance to Messrs. Samuel French, 26 Southampton Street, Strand, London, W.C.2, or their authorized representatives, who, upon payment of the fee, will send a written permission for the performance to take place. No public performance may be given unless this written permission has first been obtained.

The play takes about forty minutes in performance.

For this play dark curtains would be too rich in effect, but curtains of hessian or some similar material will serve, or a realistic " box set " may be made—a room complete except for " fourth wall," through which the audience views it. Such a set can be made of a wooden framework, covered with old newspapers or canvas and distempered. A " practical " casement window is essential, with a small platform outside, level with the sill, for the Fairy Queen to stand upon. Behind this hangings are needed, and it would be an advantage to have two sets—black or dark blue curtains in front (to represent the night), which can be drawn aside out of sight, and behind these a surface of cream or pale grey, which can be lit with red light to represent the glow of the torches. The window-curtains should be heavy, reach to the floor, hang well out from the wall, and be arranged so that they can be drawn aside from behind the scenes. In some cases it will be an advantage to have the section of scenery or curtain below the window made removable, so that Agatha can slip through to put on her dress behind the scenes ; she will have no time to lose. The window may be near the middle of the back wall, the door R. up stage, the door L. down stage, and the table left centre. The fireplace may be self-contained and constructed to stand by itself. (A small dramatic society should have several fireplaces, of different types ; stood against screens or scenery or curtains, they can be used again and again.) Red paper and an electric light globe will do for the basis of any fire, and if flames are specially desired, no doubt some member of the company will enjoy constructing them with strips of silk, kept in motion by a small *silent* electric fan concealed in the fire.

The peacock pie is something of a problem. Mr. Graham Robertson made his of buckram, covered with real pie-crust and baked, to which were attached a head made of velvet, stuffed, and a tail of large feathers painted with peacock colours. For the chestnut, a small paper-bag may be blown up and burst, off stage. (This needs rehearsal, to make sure that the sound will be convincing.) The striking mechanism of the grandfather clock should not be trusted, but a gong struck behind the scenes instead. The opening of the clock face, turning of the hands, and the striking, must be done slowly to give Agatha time to change.

Myra's dress must be white or silver, beautiful, elaborate, and loaded with jewels (from Woolworth's).

Jane's dress should be gorgeous and ridiculous. The author dressed his Fairy Godmother not as a witch, but in " fairy robes of queer, shimmering green, with a glittering crown, and long grey hair (tow) falling almost to her feet."

All the " noises off " need careful management, especially the murmurs and cheers of the crowd. Probably a Boy Scout can supply the " trumpet " calls. The music must be well chosen, and if it is not possible to have piano or violins behind the scenes, a gramophone will do. Music from *The Immortal Hour* (Columbia Gramophone Co.) is suggested.

The play needs very careful rehearsal, but is not so difficult as it appears, because its stage-craft is so good. It plays even better than it reads. The acting part on which the play hangs is Jimmy's, and this must be well cast. The producer who thinks of attempting the play may be encouraged to learn that the sensation of the first production was the Fairy Godmother—" a really amazing and most eerie performance by a boy of eight or nine."

ELDORADO

The fee for each and every representation of this play by amateurs is one guinea, payable in advance to Messrs. Samuel French, 26 Southampton Street, Strand, London, W.C.2, or their authorized representatives, who, upon payment of the fee, will send a written permission for the performance to take place.

No public performance may be given unless this written permission has first been obtained.

Time for acting, about half an hour.

Mr. Gilbert's stage directions, stage-plan, and descriptions of the characters are so detailed that they leave very little to add in the way of acting notes. It may be advisable to point out, however, that the stage-setting, which at first appears to be very difficult, can be made very simple. A stage hung with curtains will serve very well, and hessian is suggested as a suitable (and cheap) material. If " practical " windows and doors can be included, so much the better, but they are not essential.

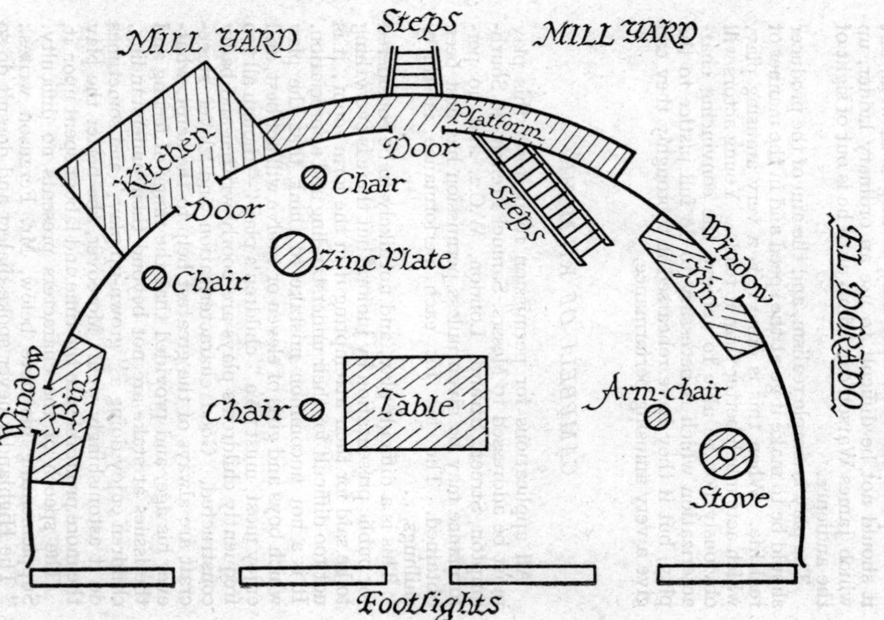
EL DORADO
MILL YARD
Steps
MILL YARD
Kitchen
Platform
Door
Door
Chair
Steps
Zinc Plate
Chair
Window
Bin
Window
Bin
Chair
Table
Arm-chair
Stove
Footlights

The steps to the next floor may be dispensed with, but it should not be difficult to use an ordinary ladder, up which James Watson can climb until he is out of sight of the audience.

The play is simple realism, and the aim of the producer should be to make it go at the speed and in the manner of real life. When this is done it is a very amusing play, which acts much better than it reads. Young actors will obviously not be able to achieve the convincing characterization which is necessary to do full justice to the play, but if they have rehearsed it thoroughly they can give a very amusing performance.

CAMPBELL OF KILMOHR

All applications for permission to perform this play must be addressed to Messrs. Samuel French, 26 Southampton Street, Strand, London, W.C.2, and no performance may be given unless permission has first been obtained. The fee for each performance is thirty shillings.

This is a difficult play, and not likely to be considered for public presentation by juniors, but there is everything to be said for their attempting it in the form room; it is not too difficult for their understanding and appreciation. It is a not uncommon mistake to think that the play which boys and girls of eleven or twelve will act best, and enjoy most, must be a " children's play "—though all too frequently children's plays are poorly written and badly constructed. Good characterization and clever stagecraft are always of the greatest help to the actor, whatever his age, and provided that the range of feeling and the issues at stake are not beyond their understanding, children enjoy doing a " grown-up play," and sometimes do it astonishingly well. Moreover, the better the play the more profitable are the time and labour spent upon it.

The speech of the characters presents no difficulty. Supplementing his note below, Mr. Ferguson writes: " The Highlander never spoke dialect and doesn't do so now, in spite of both Scott and Stevenson. He learned English as a foreign language, but carried into his spoken use of it the idiom of his own Gaelic. And any player who follows this idiom, supplied for him in the text, can keep to his own pronunciation of the words, and be assured that he is adequately representing the original." Representation is sufficient : exact reproduction is not needed.

Author's Notes

In producing any serious play it is essential to get a clear conception of the characters in it. Here the play turns on the struggle between two sharply contrasted personalities.

Archibald Campbell, a typical eighteenth-century Edinburgh lawyer, knows not only how to browbeat and bully, but also, when occasion calls, how to wheedle and persuade. He is an expert on the baser side of human nature, glib of words and fond of resounding phrases, which he rolls off *ore rotundo*. He has imagination and believes himself free from illusions. As a Campbell he belongs to a clan which never gave itself to unprofitable causes and had a genius for finding itself on the winning side.

Mary Stewart, the old woman, is as much an unconscious idealist as Campbell is a conscious materialist. Simple, uncalculating, unsophisticated peasant as she is, she is a Highland peasant, and therefore quick, sensitive, and passionate.

Out of the conflict between the two comes the tragedy. About that tragedy two things should be carefully noted. First, that Mary Stewart has no sense of defeat, and, second, that Campbell's triumph is far more apparent than real.

But the first is much the more important in the production. Indeed, it is by revealing Mary Stewart's glory in her sacrifice that the play is lifted into the realm of true tragedy. And any failure to make her sense of triumph manifest in her last speech will reduce the play to melodrama, and make it what is called a "sad" play. Tragedy, it may be observed, is never sad or depressing when it shows us the human spirit in some moment of grandeur. On the contrary, it thrills us; and by revealing some particular strength in our common human nature in some imaginary conflict, fortifies us for our own real if smaller distresses. For these reasons, special care must be given to Mary Stewart's last speech. It must have exaltation. Up to the phrase, " High will his name be with the teller of fine tales," she almost declaims the words, a certain proud dignity in her tone. But after that the pace quickens, with a touch of *wildness*, as if she were " fey," while she recapitulates what has happened. At her summing up of the situation, however, in " There are things greater than death," she returns to the tone with which she began. The last words of the play, " Let us go out . . . " are quiet, with all the " grandeur " gone out of her voice, as she accepts the fact of death and sees a duty to be done. Support in this long speech is got if Morag avoids convulsive sobbing and, as was the Celtic habit, lets her sorrow find utterance in a low continuous moan or wail, while rocking herself to the rhythm of the old woman's words. But this " keening " should cease with " Let them that are children shed the tears."

The second point in the production is to make it evident that Campbell's triumph is more apparent than real. Though of far less importance than the first point, it has much to do with a delicately balanced and finished production of the play. Can you get your audience to remember that Morag does not really know where the fugitives are, but only *thinks* she knows ? (Notice how markedly this is emphasized in the scene between mother and son early in the play by the frequent reiteration of the word " tell.") When Sandeman goes out the girl is sitting huddled up on a low stool, apart. She sits with her head bent and covered by her shawl. She should try to get herself forgotten, overlooked. As far as possible she should blend with her background. Then when the moment comes when she lifts her face and echoes Campbell's " Dead ! " the audience is as much startled as Campbell himself. After that her previous rigid stillness will be understood ; inside the girl a silent struggle had been going on as to whether she will tell or not. Campbell deceives her with his promise, and is himself, innocently, deceived by Morag—though he will only know it later.

Length of Performance.—A good production occupies not less than thirty-five minutes. It opens very slowly and quietly till Dugald appears. This leaves scope for the pace to quicken when necessary afterwards. But in a tersely written play like this remember that an audience needs time to take in the points. Therefore the danger is that of being too rapid rather than of being too slow.

Costume.—Archibald Campbell, dark coat and knee breeches of the period, with white cravat and ruffles; tricorn hat, riding cloak, and boots. James Mackenzie, similar, but not so fine; no ruffles or riding boots. Soldiers (usually three), long scarlet coats and white cross-belts, long gaiters, preferably black, tricorn hats. Captain Sandeman, similar, but crimson sash in place of cross-belt, and gold lace on hat, sword and riding boots. Women, skirts of any rough dark stuff with dark tartan shawl crossed in front and tucked into waist. Anything white or fancy is a fatal mistake. The women's "fineness" is internal, not external. Dugald Stewart, kilt of dark tartan, dark plain shirt and hose, leather belt with dirk in sheath.

Lighting.—As a high even lighting will produce a theatrical effect when thrown on so much colour, the lighting should be carefully studied. Where facilities exist throw the roof into shadow. Try to get shadows somewhere, to give depth and atmosphere. For the same reason all who enter from the storm should carry something of it in with them—say a powdering of snow or some sign of fatigue. Avoid the spick and span.

Highland Speech.—The fact that the peculiarities of Highland spoken English lie chiefly in the form of the sentences and the order of the words makes it easy to reproduce, infinitely easier than any English dialect. An occasional slight stressing of sibilants where they occur at the end of a word ("wass" for "was") would certainly be enough to recall Highland speech to any one familiar with it. Men like Campbell did of course acquire lowland Scots words and expressions such as "birze yont" ("press forward"), but such words of the sort which come in this play have been selected for their phonetic quality—they are, that is, Scots words which are pronounced as written.

J. A. Ferguson.

CATHERINE PARR

Permission to perform this play must be obtained in advance from The Collection Bureau, The Society of Authors, 84 Drayton Gardens, London, S.W.10. The fee is one guinea for each performance.

The play takes about ten minutes.

For *Catherine Parr* the staging is very simple. Any plain dark background, curtains, panelled wall, or screens, will serve excellently, and the only essential furniture is an antique table and three chairs, all in Tudor style if possible. The third chair can be used as a substitute for the bookcase, provided that the words "in the bookcase" are omitted from King Henry's speech on page 152. The articles required for the table are two boiled eggs in small cups or bowls (not modern egg-cups), antique-looking platters, pewter mugs, and a jug of "beer," a long, tapering loaf of bread (called "Vienna bread" by some bakers), and spoons and knives. Any old printed book will do for the Plutarch, the pages of which need not be seen by the audience. The play can very well be given in the open air, and there is no difficulty about the entry or the final exit.

Dresses are fully described under Shakespeare's *Henry VIII.* in *The Bankside Costume Book* (see page 227), besides appearing in the illustrations of many costume and history books.

A portrait of Catherine Parr can be found and copied, but she is not a well-known figure. In the case of Henry VIII., however, it is important that he should be made up and padded to resemble Hans Holbein's famous portrait. (See frontispiece to *Social England*, Vol. III.) If the actor has a fairly round face the resemblance can be made very close indeed.

The stage movements of the characters are few and simple, but there must be more than those indicated by the dramatist. For instance, King Henry should be asked to decide at what point he will sit down after referring to the Plutarch ; and his decision accepted, unless the producer feels strongly that it is wrong. Henry and Catherine should sit sideways to the audience, with the table between them. At the appropriate point an effective movement is for Catherine to fling herself round in her chair so that she faces the audience and speaks almost over her shoulder to Henry. Both spring to their feet, of course, when the quarrel reaches its height.

The play has a particular interest to the producer and to the young actor as an exercise in *tempo*. Success will depend to a large extent upon the producer's discernment in deciding the varying speeds at which the dialogue is to be spoken. And the interruptions must really be interruptions, as they are too rarely with amateur actors. With vigorous performance this play can be most successful.

A word of warning on one point may be useful. In a performance for which the present writer was responsible, Henry VIII. (aged 12) was an almost exact reproduction in miniature of his great original. When the curtain disclosed him cracking his egg, the audience laughed at him so loudly and so long that both he and Catherine (who greatly appreciated the play and their own appearance) broke down, and had to join in the laughter. This had not been anticipated, and naturally the actors had difficulty in recovering their gravity. It would be well to warn young players that this may happen, and provide them with pantomime to keep them busy until the laughter has subsided. In any case it is well for Henry not to crack his egg until the curtain is up, nor to discover its offensive state too quickly. He should peer at it, fling himself back disgustedly in his chair, and then slam down his spoon on the table as he speaks the opening line.

MICHAEL

No performance of this play may be given unless permission has been obtained in advance from the author's agents, Messrs. Curtis Brown, 7 Henrietta Street, Covent Garden, London, W.C. The fee for each performance is ten shillings and sixpence.

The play takes about thirty minutes.

Author's Note

For the first production of *Michael* special music was written by Norman O'Neill. In Scenes I. and II., when Michael smiles, his back is to the audience, and the effect of the smile is seen on the others in the room; and it was then that the string music seemed strangely to fill the air.

In Scene III. it was heard again when Michael is left alone in the dark room and the light gradually begins to shine around him. It continued as Michael spoke.

The music was all written for a string quartette, except that towards the end of the play, after Michael's words, " It seems to men that they live by care of themselves, but in truth it is Love alone by which they live," a faint trumpet call was heard. Michael lifted his arms, spoke the last words of the play, and the call was repeated, crashing out, as it were, at the very roof of the cottage.

Application for the original music should be made to Messrs. Curtis Brown. Miles Malleson.

The Author's Note disposes of the prime difficulty of the play, Michael's smile, and it will be seen that its effect upon Matryona and Simon will be the measure of its effect on the audience. There are no difficulties of characterization in the play, and boys or girls, or any sincere actors, can do well with it if they have been carefully coached and thoroughly rehearsed. Indeed, the best rendering will probably be an unsophisticated one, for the play retains much of that simplicity of spirit which marks the original story, and which constitutes so much of the appeal and the greatness of Tolstoy's best work. Michael's rather exacting part, in particular, demands a player who can act simply and who has an instinctive sense of poetry. If his long final speech has the least tone of insincerity or sanctimoniousness or theatrical straining after effect, it will be ruined. A professional actor may have the technical skill to make effective a speech which he does not believe in, or understand, but the amateur, young or old, can only compensate to some extent for his technical ignorance by sincerity and enthusiasm and hard work.

A set of hessian curtains will serve excellently for this

play, and if a " practical " door presents any difficulty it can be dispensed with by having the entrance in one corner, between the curtains, and the knocking " off." Table, bench, and stools should be of plain, unpainted wood (they might all be made in the school workshops), and plates and bowls of earthenware or wood or very plain china.

If accuracy in setting and costumes is desired, reference should be made to Max Tilke's *Costumes of Eastern Europe* (Benn, 1926), which gives coloured illustrations of the garments, and to Russian travel books. There is a useful picture on page 131 of *Folk Tales of the Nations* (Nelson). But there is no need for exact reproduction, and, to quote Mr. Malleson, " the clothes and the setting should give scope to producers with a certain amount of creative originality."

For the lighting in Scene III. a dimmer switch is almost essential, though a possible makeshift arrangement would be to have the stage lights wired in small groups, and diminish the lighting by switching off one group at a time. Whatever the method, the light must be very dim by the time the Woman begins to tell her story, and should come from the oil-lamp which is burning on the table, supplemented, if necessary, by an electric bulb, fixed somewhere above the proscenium opening, inside, and set in a funnel of tin so that its light is thrown only in a circle around the oil-lamp. When Matryona takes the lamp away, this electric bulb is dimmed until it is out (or switched off), leaving the room in darkness until the light begins to shine upon Michael, from a powerful lamp or set of lamps focused on his corner—and here again a dimmer switch is almost essential. There is very little difficulty or expense in making such a switch, and full instructions may be found in *Stage Lighting for " Little " Theatres* (see below, page 226).

SOME BOOKS FOR THE AMATEUR

"*Let's do a Play!*" Rodney Bennett. Illustrated by Hugh Chesterman. Large crown 8vo, cloth gilt. Nelson.

Plays, concerts, charades, revues, living marionettes, mock conjuring, and all kinds of amateur entertainments are dealt with in this book, from the simplest "show" got up on the spur of the moment, to the full-dress production in a public hall. Mr. Bennett proves himself an expert on rehearsal, stage-management, lighting, make-up, scenery, etc., etc., and his wide experience of amateur work with young players enables him to explain exactly how to make the best of scanty funds, very little equipment, and difficult conditions. And his book is unique because it is as useful to boys and girls "running a show on their own" as to their elders when these decide to take charge.

Ample material for a number of programmes is given in the last 140 pages, which include plays, sketches, and poems (suitable for young players of various ages from six to sixteen), by John Drinkwater, Alfred Noyes, Allan Monkhouse, Rodney Bennett, Ronald Gow, Elizabeth Fleming, P. Laflin, Rosalind Vallance, John Hampden, Mary Cousins, John Pearmain, etc., etc.

The Small Stage and its Equipment. R. Angus Wilson: with an Introduction by Sir Barry Jackson. Allen and Unwin.

This deals with all the problems of temporary and permanent stage-construction, lighting, and scenery, and is invaluable to the amateur because it offers practicable solutions.

Stage Lighting. C. Harold Ridge. Heffer.

An invaluable treatise on the art and technique of the subject, which every dramatic society should possess.

British Costume during Nineteen Centuries. Mrs. Charles A. Ashdown. Nelson.

The best single-volume history: from the time of the Britons to 1820, with a special section on ecclesiastical dress. 578 illustrations in colour and line.

Planning the Stage Wardrobe. Joyce Conyngham Green. Nelson.

A thoroughly practical little book on the designing and making of stage costumes. The writer is well acquainted with the limitations of amateur resources, both financial and technical. Here the amateur wardrobe mistress and dress-designer can learn how to make one set of costumes serve for many plays and how to ring the changes on cloak, scarf, robe, and accessories. There are twenty-three black-and-white plates illustrating about seventy costumes.

Mimes and Miming. Isabel Chisman and Gladys Wiles. Nelson.

A book for beginners as well as those who have already discovered the delights of miming. It shows *exactly* what to do, and contains fourteen varied mimes without acting fees. Illustrated with stage plans, etc.

Acting Improvised. Robert G. Newton. Nelson.

An ideal book for Social Service Clubs, etc. How to improvise exciting plays (with or without words) from stories, songs, newspaper reports, and similar sources. With examples and full details. Illustrated.

Producing School Plays. Ernest F. Dyer. Nelson.

Deals with every phase of the production and staging of plays and musical plays in schools, including chapters on the work of the producer, rehearsals, settings, scene design, lighting equipment, etc. An appendix on "How to make a switchboard," by H. Bambrough, M.Sc., and three appendixes on adjudication, etc., by John Hampden. 22 photographs of settings, etc., and 52 drawings.

Behind the Scenes. John Sommerfield. Nelson.

How a large professional theatre works ; how a play is put on ; what happens at a rehearsal ; how the stage is lit, and other details. Illustrated.

The Playwright's Craft. Harrison Owen. Nelson.

A straightforward work on the making of plays—with well-chosen examples from English, continental, and American drama. Deals with all the essentials of plots and plot-making, characterization, act architecture, dialogue, and stage management.

APPENDIX

THE PROCEDURE FOR A MOCK TRIAL

A MOCK TRIAL is a form of dramatic entertainment which can be made interesting, amusing, and instructive at the same time. Most dramatic societies will find it worth while to attempt such a trial occasionally, and since it is easier to stage and needs less rehearsal than a play, while providing much more scope for invention, it can be arranged in the schoolroom or the village hall with the expenditure of little time and, if desired, no money. But it must be arranged. The impromptu mock trial is very rarely a success.

The " crime " should be " discovered " some time in advance—though the " prisoner " must certainly be allowed out on bail !—the most important details of the story decided, and the players instructed in their various parts. If a public performance is to be given, at least one rehearsal is necessary. Speeches, evidence, etc., need not be learned word for word, but each player must know the main facts and ideas which he is to contribute to the progress of the trial, and in most cases notes may be used unobtrusively. Judge and Counsel can have this book open in front of them, with a full " plan " of the trial.

If the whole plot can be invented by the leading players or the organizer, so much the better. If not, it may be based upon a trial in a novel, such as that of Darnay in *A Tale of Two Cities* (for which eighteenth-century costume is needed) or the familiar case of Bardell *v.* Pickwick in *The Pickwick Papers* (which can be given in an adaptation of modern dress). The stories of Sherlock Holmes and other detectives provide very useful material, but public performances based on these cannot be given without permission from the owners of the copyright. Boys and girls greatly enjoy inventing a new Sherlock Holmes mystery, and providing him with a dramatic entry, accompanied by excited witnesses, in the middle of the trial, when the (innocent) prisoner is in grave danger of being convicted by circumstantial evidence. The opportunity for useful classroom work need not be emphasized.

The procedure which is summarized below is approximately that of an Assize Court. This is less familiar and more impressive than the ritual of the " Police Court," and the Assize deals with serious crimes which are suitable for a mock trial—such as arson, burglary, house-breaking, embezzlement, forgery, larceny, and making false coin and banknotes. It is suggested that a mock trial might be very profitably followed or preceded by some work on our legal system and the function of the various courts. The necessary information can be obtained from such books as Mr. F. Swann's *Primer of English Citizenship* (Longmans, Green, and Co.).

The Assize can be arranged simply or elaborately. Though the gilded coach and the javelin-men are not available for " the legal representative of the King," there should be little difficulty in arranging for trumpeters " off " (Boy Scouts with bugles ?) to announce the entry of a Judge resplendent in scarlet and ermine (flannelette and cotton-wool).

If a stage is available, so much the better, but in either case it is necessary to have a dais for the Judge, and advisable to have a lower one for the Clerks. Draped boxes or tables will do. (Dramatic societies will find it a good plan to buy a stock of butter boxes, which are cheap, strong, and portable, and excellent for a dais. For stage use they can be painted and built into a number of different properties.) Two black-boards, a small screen, or a draped towel-horse will do for the witness-box, and two long desks or forms for the Jury. The " bar " to which the prisoner is called can be a thin pole or brass rod lashed to two uprights—chairs will do.

The Judge wears a flowing scarlet robe trimmed with ermine ; the Clerk and Counsel wear university gowns, if available, with stiff collars (but no tie), and bands—*i.e.* two narrow strips of white linen hanging from the collar in front. If uniforms can be borrowed or improvised for policemen and warders or wardresses, so much the better, but these are not so important. There should be as much variety as possible in the dress, make-up, and manner of the prisoner and witnesses, who can be of widely different ages, classes, and nationalities.

When everything is ready, and the jury and audience are seated, the Assize proceeds as follows:

[*Enter the Usher.*]

Usher [*proclaiming loudly*]. Oyez! Oyez! Oyez! All manner of persons having aught to do before His Majesty the King and the Lords Justices of Assize draw near and give their attendance.

[*Enter the Clerk of Assize, the Counsel for the Prosecution, the Counsel for the Defence, and the Judge. Every one present rises as the Judge enters, and remains standing until he has taken his seat.*

Enter the Prisoner, guarded [*if a man*] *by two Warders, or* [*if a woman*] *by two Wardresses.*

Every one except the Judge rises when speaking.]

Clerk of Assize [*rising and reading the charge*]. "John Doe is charged that on the 8th day of December 1926, at . . . in the County of . . . he did feloniously . . . against the peace of our Lord the King his crown and dignity." Prisoner at the Bar, you have heard the Charge. Do you plead Guilty or Not Guilty?

Prisoner. Not Guilty.

Clerk of Assize. John Doe, the names I am about to call are those of the Jury who will try you. If you object to any of them, you must do so before they are sworn, and your objection will be heard.

[*The members of the Jury rise. The Clerk of Assize reads the twelve names in full, the Foreman's first—e.g. Thomas Henry Wilkinson, Frederick Jones, etc.*

The Prisoner having made no objection, the Clerk reads the words of the oath which the Jury are to take.*]

Clerk of Assize. You shall well and truly try the issue joined between our Sovereign Lord the King and the Prisoner at the Bar whom you shall have in charge, and true verdict give according to the evidence.†

* If he does object to any juryman it should be for some absurd reason.

† The words "so help you God" are here omitted.

[*As the last words of the oath are pronounced, the Jury raise their right hands, and then sit. The Counsel for the Prosecution rises.*]

Counsel for Prosecution outlines the crime of which he intends to prove the Prisoner guilty, and then announces the name of his first witness—*e.g.* William Warburton.

Judge's Clerk [*calling*]. William Warburton !

William Warburton enters, and goes into the witness-box. The Judge's Clerk gives him [*and every witness who follows*] *a card on which the words of the oath are printed.*]

William Warburton [*reading the oath slowly and solemnly*].* The evidence that I shall give between our Sovereign Lord the King and the Prisoner at the Bar shall be the truth, the whole truth, and nothing but the truth.*

Counsel for Prosecution proceeds to question the Witness, trying to elicit evidence which will show that the Prisoner is guilty. The Witness answers as clearly and briefly as possible, except when a touch of humour is desired.

[*During the examination the Judge may ask questions on any point which he thinks needs explanation, for his own benefit or that of the audience. When the Counsel for the Prosecution has finished with the Witness he sits down and the Counsel for the Defence rises.*]

Counsel for Defence proceeds to cross-examine the Witness, with a view to weakening or disproving the evidence which he has given previously, and obtaining evidence in favour of the Prisoner.

[*When Counsel for the Defence has finished, he sits, and Counsel for the Prosecution either asks further questions or gives the Witness leave to go. When this is given Witness leaves the box and takes a seat near by. Except when giving evidence no Witness is allowed in court, but this rule need not be enforced.*]

[*When all Witnesses for the Prosecution have been heard :*]

Counsel for Prosecution. That is my case, my Lord.

[*Sits down.*]

Counsel for Defence. I propose to call the Prisoner to give evidence, my Lord.

* The words "I swear by Almighty God" and "so help me God" are here omitted.

[*Witnesses for the Defence are then called, the Prisoner being the first.* (*He is not compelled to give evidence, but nearly always does so.*)]

[*Prisoner is taken into the witness-box by a Warder, and is sworn as a Witness. After being examined by Counsel for the Defence and cross-examined by Counsel for the Prosecution, Prisoner is taken back into the dock. All Witnesses for the Defence having been examined :*]

Counsel for Defence [*rising*] makes his longest and most important speech, beginning : " My Lord and Gentlemen of the Jury." He sums up all the evidence which tells in favour of the Prisoner, tries to discredit or refute (or passes over in silence) the evidence against him, refers to any past legal decisions which have bearing on the case, and does all in his power to influence the Jury in favour of the Prisoner by an eloquent appeal to their reason and their emotions. [*He sits.*]

Counsel for Prosecution [*rising*] makes a similar speech on the other side. [*Sits.*]

Judge [*remaining seated*]. " Gentlemen of the Jury, you have to decide whether the Prisoner on . . . did . . ." He then proceeds to give the Jury an impartial summing up of the facts which have been established by the evidence, drawing their attention to anything which he considers to be of special importance, and concludes, " Can you decide upon your verdict here, or do you wish to retire to consider it ? "

Foreman, after a brief consultation with the Jury, announces that they wish to retire, or that they do not.

[*If the Jury retire, the Court must wait until they have returned to their places ; but it is better if they can come to their decision* (*which must be unanimous*) *without retiring. When they have decided, the Judge proceeds at once.*]

Judge [*to Foreman*]. Are you agreed upon your verdict ?

Foreman. Yes, my Lord.

[*If he says that they have not been able to come to an agreement, the Judge must announce that the case will be tried again at the next Assizes.*]

Judge. Do you find the Prisoner Guilty or Not Guilty ?

[*If the verdict is Not Guilty :*]

Foreman. Not Guilty, my Lord.

Judge. John Doe, I concur in the verdict. You leave the Court without a stain on your character.

[*If the verdict is Guilty ; or Guilty with Recommendation to Mercy :*]

Foreman. Guilty, my Lord, *or* Guilty, my Lord, with Recommendation to Mercy.

Judge. " Prisoner at the Bar, you have been found guilty of a grave offence, which . . ." He points out the evil results of the particular crime, and then, tempering his remarks and sentence accordingly if the Prisoner has been recommended to mercy, he concludes, " I sentence you to . . ." [The sentence for burglary should be two years' imprisonment or three or more years' penal servitude ; for arson, penal servitude ; for forgery, imprisonment with or without hard labour, or penal servitude. The shortest period of penal servitude which can be given is three years.]

[*If the Prisoner is Not Guilty, he is free to leave the Court ; if Guilty, he is escorted to his cell by the Warders. The Court then rises, the Clerk of Assize, Counsel, etc., leaving in the order in which they entered.*]

RECORD OF A MOCK TRIAL

held by ....on...........

The Judge . . . .
Counsel for the Prosecution . ...
Counsel for the Defence . . ..
Clerk of Assize . . . .
Judge's Clerk . . . .
Usher . . . .
Prisoner ( ) . . . .
First Warder . . . .
Second Warder . . . .
Twelve Jurymen (their real names):

Foreman....................

....
....
....
....
....
....

Witnesses:

....
....
....
....
....

The Charge ....
....
The Verdict..
The Sentence..

A CHRISTMAS EPILOGUE

Rights of performance of this Epilogue are reserved, but amateurs may give performances without payment or application for permission, provided that acknowledgments to the Editor and the Publishers are made on the programme.

A CHRISTMAS EPILOGUE

CHARACTERS :

Five Boys or Girls, and Father Christmas.

[*The Christmas concert is over. The lights in the hall are switched on, and the First Boy* (*or Girl*) *appears between the curtains.*]

First Boy. Heap on more wood ! The wind is chill ;
But let it whistle as it will,
We'll keep our Christmas merry still.
Each age has deemed——

Second Boy [*standing up at the back of the hall, and shouting*]. Here ! You stop that !

First Boy. Why ? What for ?

Third Boy [*half-way down the hall, standing up*]. Because that's the Christmas Epilogue ! You know that, don't you ?

First Boy. Well, what about it ?

Fourth and Fifth Boys [*from different points in the audience, speaking together*]. What about it ! Nobody but Father Christmas is allowed to speak that !

Second Boy [*coming up towards the stage*]. And if any one but Father Christmas says it, all the Christmas trees in England will fall down !

[*The other boys also begin to move towards the stage.*]

Fourth Boy. And all the nuts and oranges will go bad !

Third Boy. And all the Christmas puddings will swell up and burst !

Fifth Boy. And Father Christmas will go to Chicago and stay there !

Second Boy. So you'd better be careful, my lad.

[*By this time they have all reached the front, and stand in a group, looking up at the First Boy. He stoops over the footlights to speak to them.*]

First Boy [*aghast*]. But what can we do? We *must* have an Epilogue!

Fifth Boy. Have you asked Father Christmas to come and say it?

First Boy. Great Scott! I never thought of that!

Fourth Boy. Well, you didn't expect him to come if you didn't ask him, did you?

Third Boy. It's not Christmas yet, and he must be jolly busy, anyway.

Fourth Boy. Come on, you chaps, let's call him!

Second Boy. Good idea.

All [*facing the audience, and calling*]. Father Christmas! Fa—ther Christmas! [*They listen intently for a moment.*]

Second Boy. Nothing doing.

First Boy. Perhaps he's offended, and won't come.

Third Boy. Not he! He's a jolly good sort. He doesn't get offended.

Fifth Boy. Perhaps he's a long way away. Let's try again.

All. Father Christmas! Father Christmas!

[*They listen again.*]

First Boy. I can't hear anything—can you?

Fourth and Fifth Boys. No.

Third Boy. I know. There isn't any chimney in this place. He can't get in!

[*If there is a chimney, this speech should be, ' I know! We ought to have shouted up the chimney!" and the next four speeches should be omitted, and they all go and call up the chimney.*]

Fourth Boy. Well, that's settled it!

Second Boy. I'm not so sure. He must have found other ways of getting in, what with all this central heating and jerry-built houses with chimneys that any one would get stuck in!

Fifth Boy. Oh, let's try once more, anyhow.

First Boy. Oh yes, come on!

All. Father Christmas! Father Christmas!

[*They listen. There is a faint, far-away tinkle of little bells.*]

First Boy. Hooray! Listen!

[*They listen again. The bells sound nearer. A voice is heard singing a carol.*]

First Boy. Hooray! He's coming!

[*All lights are switched off. In the darkness the First Boy slips through the curtains and disappears ; the others withdraw to the sides of the hall. The curtains part and Father Christmas appears, carrying a brilliant red lantern which throws its light upon his head and shoulders.*]

Father Christmas. Heap on more wood ! the wind is chill ; *
But let it whistle as it will,
We'll keep old Christmas merry still.
Each age has deemed the new-born year
The fittest time for festal cheer
E'en, heathen yet, the savage Dane
At Yule more deep the mead did drain ;
And well our Christian sires of old
Loved when the year its course had rolled,
And brought blithe Christmas back again,
With all his hospitable train.
Domestic and religious rite
Gave honour to the holy night ;
On Christmas Eve the bells were rung ;
On Christmas Eve the mass was sung ;
The damsel donned her kirtle sheen ;
The hall was dressed with holly green ;
Forth to the wood did merry men go
To gather in the mistletoe.
Then opened wide the baron's hall
To vassal, tenant, serf, and all ;
Power laid his rod of rule aside,
And Ceremony doffed his pride.
All hailed, with uncontrolled delight,
And general voice, the happy night
That to the cottage, as the crown,
Brought tidings of salvation down.
The huge hall table's oaken face,
Scrubbed till it shone, the day to grace,
Then was brought in the lusty brawn,
By old blue-coated serving-man ;
Then the grim boar's head frowned on high,
Crested with bays and rosemary.
There the huge sirloin reeked ; hard by

* The first forty-nine lines are taken from *Marmion*

Plum-porridge stood, and Christmas pie;
Nor failed old England to produce,
At such high tide, her savoury goose.
Then came the merry maskers in,
And carols roared with blithesome din;
White shirts supplied the masquerade,
And smutted cheeks the visors made;
But oh! what maskers richly dight
Can boast of bosoms half so light!
England was merry England, when
Old Christmas brought his sports again.
'Twas Christmas broached the mightiest ale;
'Twas Christmas told the merriest tale;
A Christmas gambol oft could cheer
The poor man's heart through half the year.
So here come I to wish you all
The joys of Christmas festival,
Good cheer as in old days gone by,
Glad hearts, free minds, and good mince-pie,
A happy family round the fire,
And unto each his heart's desire.

[*The little bells are heard again.*

My reindeer scents the Lapland snow;
The sleigh-bells jingle; I must go,
For many a village, many a town,
Before the Christmas stars go down,
Awaits my blessing on its glee,
That joy may reign from sea to sea.
Wassail! Wassail! To all, good cheer!
Old Father Christmas gives you here
A Happy Christmas, Glad New Year!

CURTAIN

PRINTED IN GREAT BRITAIN AT
THE PRESS OF THE PUBLISHERS